W9-CBK-956

SIX GREAT SCIENTISTS

COPERNICUS · GALILEO · NEWTON
DARWIN · MARIE CURIE · EINSTEIN

J. G. CROWTHER

'It is the moral qualities of its leading personalities that are perhaps of even greater significance for a generation and for the course of history than purely intellectual accomplishments. Even these latter are, to a far greater degree than is commonly credited, dependent on the stature of character.'
—Albert Einstein:
Marie Curie in Memoriam

BARNES
&NOBLE
BOOKS
NEW YORK

This edition published by Barnes & Noble, Inc.

1995 Barnes & Noble Books

ISBN 1-56619-691-4

Printed and bound in the United States of America

M 9 8 7 6 5 4

CONTENTS

INTRODUCTION

It appears, as Einstein has told us, and is evident in the stories here recounted, that the primary factors in supreme scientific achievement are moral qualities. High intellectual ability is, of course, essential, but even more important is determination, and the will to discovery. It is a striking fact that none of our six supreme scientific geniuses was a child prodigy, or even very precocious. The brightest of them in youth seems to have been Galileo, and certainly at least four of the six were not startling performers at school. Marie Curie was the most successful, she was a very determined scholar. Newton was ordinary, Darwin was considered backward, and Einstein sub-normal.

But all of them, as soon as they had found their vocation, pursued research with extraordinary concentration. Copernicus worked steadily at his great book, *The Revolutions of the Celestial Orbs*, among the numerous duties of a busy life, for thirty-six years, and received an advance copy only on his deathbed. He spent no less than ten years in the Italy of Michelangelo and the Borgias, absorbing the learning of the Renaissance, before returning to the Baltic to work out its scientific significance.

Galileo smuggled the greatest of his books out of Italy and published it abroad, when he was sixty-eight and already for many years under the surveillance of the Inquisition. Nothing could deter him, not persecution, not old age, nor approaching blindness.

Newton wrote his Mathematical *Principles of Natural*

Philosophy, the greatest of all scientific works, in fifteen months by an astounding effort of concentration, when he was closely connected with Whig politics, and about to take an important part in the rebellion against James II. He devoted far more of his energy and time to alchemy and theology than to physics and mathematics, and his overwhelming success in the description of the physical universe seems to have been the realization of only a small part of a frantic ambition to solve the riddle of existence and the secret of life.

Charles Darwin was intended first to be a medical doctor; he showed little sign of succeeding at that, so his disappointed father sent him to be educated for the Church, at which he succeeded no better. He first gained notice by an exceptional ability for collecting beetles and became a good naturalist. He was offered the post of naturalist to the *Beagle* on its voyage round the world because there was no prospect of finding a professional naturalist who could afford to be away from his job for several years. Launched on the voyage, his genius developed steadily in its serene greatness, and after the phenomena of plant and animal nature were unfolded before his eyes for three continuous years, the first idea of evolution came to his mind as he examined the astonishing variations of living things in the Galapagos Islands.

He returned from five years of martyrdom to seasickness a permanent invalid, and spent the remainder of his life, nearly forty years, secluded in the country, his days organized down to the last detail, steadily writing one masterpiece after another.

Marya Sklodovska struggled against difficult circumstances in Czarist Poland with heroic determination to achieve a scientific life. She did well at school and then, because women were not at that time admitted to Polish universities, had to work for six years as a governess, during the best years of her youth, not only to earn the money to be able to go to Paris, but also to help to pay for her elder sister to go there first. How she preserved her faith in the possibility of becoming a scientist while she was mostly isolated in the countryside, is a miracle. And when she got to Paris, a young woman, not even French, she graduated first in physics and second in mathematics at the University, beating all the ablest young French men and women of the year.

Then she discovered radium and spent three years obtaining a pure specimen. This involved months and months of boiling solutions, in charges of forty pounds weight at a time, and stirring with iron rods several feet long, all of which was done by her personally without an assistant. Finally, she died of a pernicious anaemia brought on by radium radiation. In the end, she sacrificed her life to her mighty discovery.

Einstein started earning his living as an engineering clerk in the Swiss Patent Office at Berne. He discovered the theory of relativity during his spare time at home and in the office. He used to do his research on bits of paper, and when anyone came into his room at the office, he slipped it into a drawer. It was almost like a schoolboy doing homework under the desk during a lesson. He never met a first-rate physicist until four years after he had discovered the theory of relativity.

Einstein was as courageous in life as in science. He spoke against Nazism in Germany without the shadow of a compromise, and he never ceased to warn mankind of the dangers of the misuse of science.

One thing all of these geniuses had : the determination to do scientific research, whatever the obstacles. The first factor in their achievement was their character : the will not to be defeated. The second factor they all showed was the imagination to conceive a great idea. When they had got the idea, nothing could stop them from proving that it was true.

The most outstanding quality of all these scientists was their tremendous belief in life and the possibilities of human endeavour. Their achievements and their example renew our confidence in human destiny, by reminding us of what men and women are capable when they have the ability, the determination, and the will to solve the most difficult problems.

The successes of the scientist in discovering the secrets of nature have placed astounding new powers in the hands of mankind. These have created new problems of a very serious character, even the possibility of the extermination of life itself. But the example of the will and the courage of the supreme scientists in facing their problems gives us confidence that what mankind has had the ability to bring forth, mankind will also have the will and the courage to control.

NICOLAUS COPERNICUS
1473 - 1543

COPERNICUS was the founder of the modern conception of the universe. He was the inaugurator of the scientific age in which we live. We owe our modern scientific way of looking at things more to him than to any other man, and in this sense his achievement was more important, and of a higher order than that of any of his successors. There have been many who were better mathematicians and experimenters, and much more skilful in making technical use of the new point of view, but he was its author.

He was the first to believe with complete certainty that the earth revolves round the sun, and support his arguments with sufficient proof.

Since immemorial times, men had believed that the heavens revolved round the earth. This seemed self-evident. As they looked at the stars they saw the whole universe circling round themselves. Man was the centre of creation, and the world was made for him.

Copernicus showed that this was an illusion. In fact, man was the inhabitant of a tiny planet revolving around the sun, in a vast ocean of space populated by immeasurably distant stars. He shattered the ancient human egocentric conception of the universe, and revealed mankind's true place in it. He gave men one of their very greatest accessions of self-knowledge and enabled them, not only to look at the heavens, but at all of their beliefs and activities, with a new objectivity. He helped them to grow up and acquire an adult view of existence. His work stimulated the questioning of generally accepted ideas in religion, philosophy and sociology, as well as in science. Some men soon pushed the implications of his conclusions as far as they would go, and Giordano Bruno, the boldest of these, was burned at the stake for his pains by the Inquisition on February 17th 1600.

Why was Copernicus able to do such an extraordinary thing? Where did he come from? What were the circumstances which provided the stage on which his genius could play such a magnificent part?

He was born at Torun, a port on the river Vistula near the Baltic coast in Poland, on February 19th 1473. At that time, this region was regarded as on the fringe of civilized Europe. Copernicus himself described his home on the Baltic coast as 'this very remote corner of the earth in which I live'. How was his tremendous achievement accomplished in a region apparently so isolated? Why was it possible that a work which affected all mankind and future ages so deeply could have been done there? We have to look into the background of Copernicus' life to find the answers to these questions.

Copernicus' father came from Cracow. He settled in Torun, where he married, and where his son Nicolaus was born. He was a substantial copper merchant, accustomed to considerable financial business. In 1454, the townsmen of Danzig gave Copernicus Senior one thousand Hungarian gulden to secure their recognition as good Polish Catholics by the Cardinal of Cracow. His wife, Nicolaus' mother, was Barbara Watzelrode, the daughter of a well-to-do Torun merchant and Polish patriot. Her sister married Tilman von Allen, who was mayor of Torun, and her brother Lucas became an eminent churchman.

Barbara Watzelrode's father bequeathed to her husband

and herself a little property of more than twelve acres, with house, sheds, vineyard, silver and gold, and chattels. Nicolaus spent his childhood in these comfortable surroundings. His father led a gentlemanly life, engaging in property deals and lawsuits.

Torun was not, in fact, as isolated as it appeared. As a shipping town, it was a member of the Hanseatic League. It was a link through which Poland, Hungary and Western Europe exchanged merchandize with Venice and Novgorod, Nuremberg, Bruges and Bergen. Torun had representatives in London, and in Denmark it had the extraterritorial right of appointing judges for the trial of its own citizens. In Copernicus' childhood, Torun was a town of 20,000 inhabitants, with an international trade.

Nicolaus and the other boys no doubt spent hours at the river wharves, listening to the stories of the sailors of the Hansa ships coming from distant regions of the world. He had good opportunities for learning some of the practical lessons of the new geography, of trade and exploration, and of the globe of the earth as a real object, not merely as a hypothetical sphere.

Nicolaus Copernicus was a son of the new merchants, with their far-flung trade. When he was ten years old, his father died, and his uncle Lucas, the churchman, became his guardian. Lucas Watzelrode was at that time a canon of the Catholic Church. He placed his brother's children under church protection, and he directed Nicolaus' education. He sent him, at the age of nineteen, to study at his own university, Cracow, in 1492.

It is significant that Copernicus' studies began in the year of the discovery of America. His mind began to mature in one of the most exciting and stimulating moments in history. He started to think in the atmosphere of anticipation created by the discovery of a new continent, and the virtual doubling of the known world. The discovery of America gave practical proof that the earth was a sphere. This eased Copernicus' future flights of imagination.

His uncle Watzelrode had studied at Cracow when he was sixteen, and had sold one of his inheritances to obtain the means to go to Bologna to study law. He became friendly with Callimachus, the Italian humanist who had taken part in a plot against the Pope's life, with the aim of abolishing Christianity and reviving the Roman Republic. When the plot failed, Callimachus, whose original name was Buonaccorsi, fled to Poland, where he joined with the Queen, Bona Sforza, in intrigues and exploitation. He became Polish ambassador to the Sultan of Turkey.

Watzelrode had studied in Italy and knew Rome. He was widely educated and travelled. He had acquired the spirit of the Renaissance, and combined it with natural political ability. He was a canon of Frauenburg, the church of the Varmian diocese, whose bishop was the virtual ruler of Prussia, in this period of prince-bishops.

When the Bishop of Varmia died, Watzelrode was in Rome, probably by design, and was immediately consecrated Bishop of Varmia, before the King of Poland was able to appoint his own son Frederick to the place. Shortly afterwards, the king died, and his son Jan Albert, who had been tutored by Callimachus, now wrote to Watzelrode for support in the election to the vacant throne.

Jan Albert, Watzelrode and Callimachus were fervent Polish patriots who hated the knights of the Teutonic Order, and set out to make Poland the greatest power in Europe. Its frontiers were extended from the Baltic to the Black Sea.

Copernicus' uncle was one of the ablest and most powerful men in Poland, and for a long period in Polish history was much more celebrated than Nicolaus. Contemporary portraits show him as a strong man, perhaps a little brutal, with big round features, and large staring eyes. He secured every advantage for his nephew. He appointed him a canon of Frauenburg before he had completed his studies, so Copernicus had an assured income from the age of twenty-four, for the rest of his life. Canons did not then necessarily have religious duties, and it was not unusual for them to be appointed, and then sent away by the Chapter to be educated for their work, whether lay or religious.

At Cracow, Copernicus was taught by Brudzewski, who was one of the best mathematicians and astronomers of his day, and had edited the works of Purbach and Regiomontanus. At that time, Cracow was an important centre of exchange between Europe and Russia and Asia, and its university was the best in northern Europe. Callimachus had established flourishing Greek studies there, and the Cracow scholars were in the forefront of learning.

Copernicus probably left Cracow at the end of 1494, after receiving a good training, which he always remembered with gratitude. After his appointment as canon, he did not return home permanently to perform his duties, but was given leave of absence for further study. He entered the University of Bologna in 1496, and spent no less than ten years in Italy, in the time of the Borgian Pope Alexander VI, Cesar Borgia himself, Savonarola, Ludovico Sforza Duke of Milan, Leonardo da Vinci, Michelangelo and Machiavelli.

When he studied at Bologna, the university was at the height of its fame. Thousands of students from all parts of Europe came to it, and the city spent half of its public revenue in supporting it. This policy paid handsomely, for many of the wealthy students came with retinues of servants, and lived extravagantly. There were large numbers of older, post-graduate students, who returned to the university to refresh their knowledge, and some were gentlemen settled there indefinitely, studying the new learning as a fashionable social pleasure. Even the clerical students were gay, for they lived and dressed like the others, except when attending church services. They ordinarily wore the sword and bright hat of young gentlemen, and were indistinguishable from the rest.

Students from abroad were registered according to nationality or native language, and strictly supervized. They were organized in fraternities which were called ' nations '. Students had considerable freedom of choice of the one to which they would belong, and did not always join the ' nation ' of their own country or language. In Copernicus' time, there were eighteen ' nations ' of students from countries beyond the Alps, including England, France, Germany and Poland. The students in each ' nation ' elected a rector who governed them, and supervized their lodging and finances.

The German ' nation ' at Bologna took students of law only, and had special privileges. Many wealthy students joined it, even registering their tutors and servants as members, as well as themselves, so that the privileges would be extended to all.

Copernicus, who was probably bilingual, speaking both Polish and German with equal fluency, joined the German ' nation ', and his name is found in the register for 1496 as ' Dominus Nicolaus Kopperlingk de Thorn '. He seems to have entered fully into the student life, besides his studies, for he spent the whole of his income as a Frauenburg canon, and a subsidy from his uncle, and yet had to borrow a modest sum from the Frauenburg emissary in Rome, who obtained a loan for him from a bank.

Copernicus was at Bologna for four years. He does not seem to have troubled much over learning law, but pursued his interests in astronomy and mathematics and learned Greek. He was one of the first Poles to master this ancient language, which gave him the key to Greek science and enabled him to read the Greek astronomers in their own language and not in defective translations.

The main cultural influence of Copernicus' life came from Italy, the home of the Renaissance. He learned there freedom and boldness of thought and the multifarious variety of new ideas. He combined all these with his own northern steadfastness and a strong sense of intellectual realism. Most of the men of the Renaissance were Platonists and played with new ideas as ingenious fancies. This was not at all Copernicus' attitude. For him, a true scientific theory was a real part of the mechanism of the external world, the revolution of the planets round the sun was a real thing, not just an ingenious idea which helped to simplify calculations.

He also secured mainly from the north the new mathematical skill required for proving his views. It is probable that the achievements of the great German mathematician Regiomontanus were a strong inspiration to him. Both men came from lands north of the Alps, and Copernicus may have found the example of what a fellow-northerner could do an encouragement.

Regiomontanus was the Latin name of Johannes Müller, the outstanding mathematician and astronomer of the fifteenth century. He was born at Königsberg in Bavaria in 1436, and gave himself the Latin name of his native city. He was assassinated in Rome in 1476, at the age of forty, after having been summoned there by Pope Sixtus IV to aid in the reform of the calendar, a plan which was not carried out until one hundred years later.

Regiomontanus was an infant prodigy. He became a student at Leipzig University when he was eleven, and compiled a very difficult astronomical yearbook at that age. The manuscript still exists, written in his childish hand. At the age of fourteen he went to Vienna to study under Purbach, and computed the astronomical yearbook for 1451. At the age of fifteen he became astrologer to Emperor Frederick III.

Purbach and Regiomontanus developed more precise methods of deducing the time from the position of the stars, as mechanical clocks were not yet sufficiently accurate. Later, when clocks became better made, the astronomical method of computing time was used to check their performance. They made an analysis of the *Almagest*, Ptolemy's treatise on astronomy, in which the trigonometrical functions of sine and cosine were used, and a table of natural sines was included.

Regiomontanus was among the first to study the original texts of the Greek mathematicians, which were becoming available to Europeans during the fifteenth century, and he read the works of the Arabian mathematicians. As a result of these studies, he produced the first systematic textbook on trigonometry, the parent of all those volumes over which young students have since spent so many hours.

He was invited to settle in Nuremberg in 1471, then the centre of the German mechanical and artistic renaissance. An observatory was built for him, and he established a mechanics' shop for making astronomical and scientific instruments. The new astronomical tables, and the Nuremberg globes made by Behaim, were used by Diaz, Columbus and Vasco da Gama as navigational aids in their great voyages across the ocean, where they could steer only by the stars.

Regiomontanus constructed a mechanical eagle, which flapped its wings and saluted when the Emperor Maximilian I entered the city. It was regarded as one of the marvels of the age.

He did much to establish modern methods of observation. He noted the circumstances of observations, and accurately determined the time. He found the position of a planet by measuring it in relation to certain fixed stars, which he used as reference points, or coordinates. His yearbook indicated the best moments for observation, and his textbook of trigonometry simplified the calculations.

The books that he printed himself were free from the more vulgar forms of astrology, though the publishers of the later editions, after he was dead, added popular astrology to increase the sales. Regiomontanus seemed to be moving away from astrology, but owing to his spectacular talents and brief life, he acquired the reputation of a supreme wizard. The new view of modern science was strongly fermenting in him. He strenuously cultivated the soil in which Copernicus could grow to fruition, but when he died he had not yet extricated his own genius from the old medieval ideas.

In addition to studying his works, Copernicus had a more direct connection with him. His own teacher in Bologna was Maria di Novara, who had been one of Regiomontanus' pupils. Novara was a distinguished astronomical observer who re-determined the position of all stars mentioned by Ptolemy in his *Almagest*. He discovered that the aspect of the heavens had changed since antiquity. The effect was subsequently shown by Isaac Newton to be due to the gyroscopic properties of the spinning earth, which wobbles slightly, like a top. Owing to the wobble, the aspect of the heavens from a fixed place on the earth changes slightly but steadily with the centuries, so that the stellar constellations appeared in the past in quite other positions. For instance, the Southern Cross, now the most prominent constellation in the Australian sky, could be seen in the English sky six thousand years ago.

Though Novara was such a distinguished astronomer, he secured his living and fame as an astrologer. He taught at Bologna for twenty-seven years, and died in 1504, at the age of fifty.

Copernicus studied under Novara, and then collaborated with him. It is quite possible that he had lodgings in Novara's house. On March 9th 1497, they collaborated in the observation of the eclipse of the bright star Aldebaran by the moon. This was Copernicus' first important observation, and he subsequently used it to prove his theory of the motion of the moon.

He went to Rome in the great Jubilee year of 1500, and remained there for about twelve months. He must have seen the amazing crowds of pilgrims, and the men and women who came from all the Christian countries of the world, and he probably saw them blessed by the terrifying, bull-necked Borgia, Pope Alexander VI.

Few men could have had a wider education and experience. He was now an accomplished astronomer, and gave lectures on mathematics and astronomy in Rome. Some years later, in 1514, the Pope invited him to join in the still-continuing discussions on the reform of the calendar, but he did not accept this distinguished invitation. Copernicus was then forty-one, and already had an international reputation. He was far from being an obscure man.

He returned to Frauenburg in 1501, after his leave of absence to study in Bologna had ended. He had not taken a degree in law, and he agreed to study medicine, to be of service to his church brethren. This was not so strange a proposal then as it would seem to us now, as the belief in astrology, and of the influence of the stars on health, was universal. A knowledge of astronomy appeared at that time to be a good grounding for medical practice.

Before Copernicus introduced the modern view of the

universe, the ancient doctrine of the macrocosm and the microcosm had dominated men's ideas for centuries. There was supposed to be a parallel between the happenings in the macrocosm or universe, with those in the microcosm or man. The health and fate of men was linked with events in the heavens. Study of the stars would reveal their fortune and destiny. Astrology was consequently a very important business. No religious, political, or military, or even intellectual decision could be taken without consulting its practitioners. As long as the macro- and microcosm theory was accepted, this was a rational conclusion. The theory, which seems so fantastic to the modern mind, was based on the view that man is the centre of the universe, which revolves round him. When this was shown to be illusory, the foundation of astrology collapsed. Thus Copernicus undermined astrology, besides advancing the science of astronomy. His achievement was immensely more important than merely clever astronomical observations and calculations.

Unlike nearly all other astronomers of his time, Copernicus never practised astrology. He did not read horoscopes, nor make forecasts, or interpretations of conjunctions of the planets. A quarter of a century after he had died, the great mathematician Cardan, who was astrologer to the Pope, sought to prove his own astrological infallibility by starving himself to death, in order to confirm his own forecast of the event. Even Kepler, a century later, made most of his income throughout his life from the sale of prophecies. He called astrology 'the foolish and disreputable daughter of astronomy, without which the wise old mother would starve'.

Copernicus was protected from this temptation, not only by his austere scientific judgment, but also by his assured income from the Church.

The destruction of the doctrine of the macrocosm and

the microcosm, which was the basis of medieval teaching concerning man and the world, released human health and activities from supposed dependence on the stars, so that they could become objects of investigation in their own right. This led to the development of the new independent sciences of biology and sociology.

The micro- and macrocosm theory was part of the fixity of the static feudal order, and until men were released from it they could not acquire a strong sense of the notion of change, and of being in command of their own destinies. By abolishing the apparent basis of this ancient theory, Copernicus made it possible for Shakespeare to write:

> The fault, dear Brutus, is not in our stars,
> But in ourselves, that we are underlings . . .

Copernicus did not set out consciously to advance such ends. As his knowledge of astronomy was a qualification, from the old astrological point of view, to study medicine, he was sent back to Italy to complete his medical training. In later life, his medical practice was an important part of his daily work. He was completely conventional in his practice, and prescribed the typically horrible medieval medicines. Most of his recipes came from Avicenna. Among his papers are notes on Arnoldus de Villa Nova's Imperial Pills, which 'may be taken at any time . . . and have a curative effect on every disease . . .'

One recipe which he noted twice contained twenty-two ingredients, including silver, gold, sapphires, emeralds, pearls, the rind of a lemon tree, coal, vinegar, saffron, ivory, cinnamon, unicorn's horns and Armenian sponges.

He preferred that bowel movements should be stimulated by external rather than internal medicaments, and he had prepared directions for vomiting and purging, the removal of hair, the preservation of teeth, the treatment of toothache, and the dyeing of hair. He also had notes on the treatment of paralysis, stomach ache, and the plague.

He was often consulted by his royal and episcopal friends, and used to call on them in a coach drawn by six horses. He gave his medical services without payment, and had a large free practice among the poor, on account of which he was much respected by them.

Though his own medical practice was quite old-fashioned, his revolutionary advance in astronomy indirectly helped to modernize medicine, by stimulating the scientific development of every branch of knowledge.

The Frauenburg Chapter granted Copernicus two more years of leave to study medicine. Once again he happily arranged his affairs for a sojourn in Italy, going first to Padua, whose medical school was famous. Then he went to Ferrara, where the heir to the dukedom, Alfonso d'Este, and his wife Lucrezia Borgia, were flourishing. There he remedied his lack of a legal degree, and received his doctorate of canon law from the Archbishop of Ferrara, another of the Borgias. After this, he went back to Padua to continue his medical studies.

Finally, after ten years of study in Italy, he returned home at the age of thirty-three, learned in the mathematics, astronomy, law and medicine of the day, and a competent painter; a fine Polish master of the culture of the Renaissance. In Strasbourg Cathedral there is a copy of a copy of his self-portrait.

The Chapter of Frauenburg gave him still further leave to serve his uncle the Bishop in his magnificent palace at Heilsberg, which was ten miles from the cathedral. Nicolaus became his secretary, personal physician, confidant and protégé. Watzelrode seemed to be grooming him to succeed himself as Bishop. From 1506 until his uncle's death in 1512, he lived with him as a son. He participated in the conduct of political and diplomatic affairs at one of the highest sources, and he had time for private scientific studies.

At Heilsberg he had leisure to translate Greek literary works into Latin, and make astronomical observations. He made a Latin translation of the letters of the Byzantine Greek writer Theophylactus Simocatta. This was printed in Poland, and was the first example of a Greek work being put into print in Poland before it had been printed in any other country. It was the first time that a Polish scholar had gained such a precedence for his country's learning.

Copernicus' first cultural contribution, published in 1509, was made to literature. It was typical of a Renaissance humanist. But in a poetical introduction to this work, written by Corvinus, the contemporary town clerk of Wroclaw, there are references to the translator's astronomical studies, to his investigations of the rapid motion of the moon, of the changing motion of the planets, and of his elucidation of things from amazing principles.

These are the earliest references to Copernicus' astronomical ideas. Corvinus had been one of his teachers at Cracow. Copernicus probably made the first projects for his scientific masterpiece when he was at Heilsberg.

When at last he found himself permanently established at Frauenburg, which was his residence for the remaining thirty years of his life, this little cathedral town had a population of about fourteen hundred. It is on the Frische Haff, a fresh-water lagoon formed by a bar of sand dunes, about a mile off the Baltic coast. Tributaries of the Vistula flow into the lagoon, and keep its waters sweet.

The cathedral is on a hill about eighty feet high. Copernicus lived in a strong red brick tower surrounded by oaks and elms, which a little higher than the rest of the building. From this he had an unobstructed view for observations. He could see far over the plains, and over the sea beyond the quiet lagoon, watching the stars rise and set, but often losing them in the low-lying mists. He made more than half of the personal observations quoted in his *Revolutions of the Celestial Spheres* at Frauenburg.

He did not, however, live the life of a recluse. The regime at Frauenburg was not monastic. Most of the sixteen canons were absent, acting as men-of-affairs, businessmen and diplomats. The Chapter owned one-third of the province of Varmia. His most intimate friend, Tiedemann Giese, who was seven years his junior, was a fellow canon. After studying at Leipzig, Giese had become secretary of the King of Poland, and canon of Frauenburg. He and Copernicus were at Frauenburg together for a generation. In 1538 Giese was appointed Bishop of Kulm.

He was a spokesman of the Catholic liberals, and sought to mediate between the two conflicting religious movements. He was a kind and affectionate man, who found the essence of Christianity in faith and love. He secured Copernicus' approval for one of his pamphlets aimed at bringing peace to the Church. He corresponded with Erasmus, and maintained friendly relations with the German reformers, in order to try to bring them back to the Church.

As befitted Copernicus' friend, he was learned in astronomy. After Rheticus visited Giese he reported that 'He owns a bronze armillary sphere for observing equinoxes, like the two somewhat larger ones which Ptolemy says were at Alexandria and which learned men from everywhere in Greece came to see. He has also arranged that a gnomon[1] truly worthy of a prince should be brought to him from England. I have examined this instrument with the greatest pleasure, for it was made by an excellent workman who knew his mathematics'.

[1] Astronomical time-piece.

The canons of Frauenburg were administrators, scholars, scientists and men-of-the-world. Watzelrode had had an illegitimate son, and several of the canons, including Copernicus, were accused of misconduct with their housekeepers. These accusations were made by the light-minded and venal Bishop Dantiscus, the gifted son of a Danzig brewer, who wrote notoriously erotic poetry and had illegitimate children in his youth, and in his later years made charges against his subordinates, to demonstrate his righteousness and curry favour with the increasingly reactionary powers in Rome. When Copernicus was an old man of sixty-six, he had a young and good-looking housekeeper named Anna Schillings. Dantiscus accused him on the ground that Anna was too young and attractive for her position. But such evidence as exists is all in favour of Copernicus. His nature was grave and preoccupied, and whatever his relations with Anna Schillings may have been, they were probably in the best character of the times in which he lived.

Copernicus never took the higher degrees of religious ordination. He was engaged in lay duties, and acted for the Chapter as a district administrator and negotiator. In 1520 the Chapter appointed him to the governorship of Allenstein Castle. He had to defend it against a siege by the Teutonic knights, and he carried out this military operation successfully.

He made detailed accounts of the peasants' possessions, and drew up regulations for controlling the price of bread. This concern with the economic life of the community brought him in contact with the problem of monetary reform. The stream of gold from the New World was producing inflation throughout Europe. In Prussia the situatior was exacerbated by the struggles for power between the German and the Polish interests. Prices rose, and the conditions of the church's tenants worsened. Copernicus was thoroughly acquainted with the facts, and he analyzed their meaning profoundly.

In the course of these studies, he noticed, as Aristophanes had done long ago, that bad money drives out good, and he formulated this law twenty-two years before Gresham, after whom it is generally named. 'A greater mistake, however, is to introduce new, bad money beside the old, good money, for the bad not only devalues the old, better currency but drives it away'.

He was in favour of a new uniform currency for the whole of Prussia and Poland, and he read a memorandum of his views to the Prussian Diet in 1519. But the representatives of Danzig and the other cities would not accept them. They regarded the right to mint their own money as a mark of their independence. In Poland, however, his advice was taken, to the great benefit of the country. He said that the introduction of new inferior coins, at the same value as the old, was 'an insufferable error'. The ruler who did this cheated himself as well as his subjects, and behaved like a mean farmer who sowed bad seed in order to save good. In Prussia the goldsmiths alone profited from the debased currency, for they bought the old gold coins from unintelligent people, and separated the silver from them.

He suggested that one mint should be established for the whole of Prussia, and not more than twenty marks should be coined from each pound of fine silver. His advice was not accepted, and the general confusion and social unrest continued. At this time, he was appointed general administrator of the diocese, during a vacancy in the bishopric, so he had to grapple with the social and economic difficulties of the province with full responsibility. Some years later, he was still attentive to currency problems, and in 1527 he expressed his views even more clearly. He wrote that the four main causes of the decline of states were inner dissension, high mortality, barrenness of the soil and inflation. The first three were generally understood, but the fourth was noted by only a few reflective persons, for its effects were gradual. If Prussia did not remedy her currency, she would be left with nothing but copper coins, and all foreign trade would stop. The beloved fatherland, to which they owed their lives and all they possessed, was decaying through 'brainless neglect'. The poor could not buy bread with bad coins. Only the gentlemen who make them, and a few traders, profited from them. Bad money depressed initiative, fostered laziness, and forced up the cost of living. He recommended still more vigorously monetary and economic unity, and free trade.

In 1528, when he was asked for a copy of the latest statement of his views on currency, he remarked that explanations of these matters, which are 'obscure by nature' are of considerable value. He sometimes felt that he could not make clear to others things that were clear to himself but he acknowledged freely that he could err, for he was only one man, with one mind, and did not always learn or observe what others may have thought out more effectively.

Isaac Newton in his day became the Warden of the English Mint, and also attended seriously to the theory of currency. His views on this subject have been analyzed by Shirras and Craig, who reported that they did not seem to have any special originality. It is remarkable that both Copernicus and Newton should have been seriously concerned with this subject, and that Copernicus' contribution should have been more original. It is possible that he had a traditional interest in currency, for his father the copper dealer may have been concerned in the supply of metal for coins.

Copernicus had a retiring and reflective genius, but he had an extensive experience of administration. Nor was he merely an administrator. He thought about his experiences, and drew important new theoretical conclusions from them.

Copernicus' interest in astronomy was not discouraged by the Church, which had a practical concern for the computation of accurate calendars. It needed these for the precise regulation of religious dates and festivals, and the proper conduct of the agriculture of its vast estates.

He read the conventional works and made astronomical observations when he was a youth. The critical event which enabled him to progress from the conventional astronomy of his time was his knowledge of Greek, and his discussions in Italy with astronomers who knew Greek. His teacher, Novara, besides being an excellent astronomical observer, was an ardent Platonist and Pythagorean, who tried to express the relations between the magnitudes of the universe in simple mathematical terms.

The professor of Greek at Bologna was Antonius Urceus Codrus. He was a friend of Pico della Mirandola, and a man in love with learning. He lived in poverty, being unable to spare the time to secure an adequate income, and was so devoted to Greek that he read the *Iliad* from a book on his knees while he skimmed milk with one hand, and turned his meat spit with the other. He included expositions of the Greek astronomers, and of Euclid and Archimedes, in his encyclopaedic lectures. Copernicus probably received stimulating information about the Greek astronomers from Codrus' lectures.

He began to read the Greek authors in the original and discuss them in the new critical atmosphere of the Renaissance. Two impressions were made on his mind, firstly, the perfection of the Greek astronomy in the light of the knowledge of their day, and secondly, the indubitable differences between their results and the new astronomical knowledge in the thousand years since their scientific effort had ended.

Copernicus deeply respected the greatness of the Greeks, but he equally respected these new astronomical facts. He was conscious that they had produced confusion in the ancient theories, and that some new principle was needed to restore order and simplicity in the astronomers' conception of the universe. His intellectual situation was similar to that of physicists today, who are searching for a new fundamental idea to resolve the confusion of the nucleus of the atom.

He probably heard from Novara and Codrus that the Pythagoreans, and others, had suggested that the earth went round the sun, and he decided to make a systematic search of ancient literature to see what had been said about this, and whether any other relevant idea could be found which might show a way to the resolution of the confusion in astronomy.

Copernicus has given his own description of the ideas which prompted his investigation, and how he proceeded with it, in the introduction to his great book *De Revolutionibus Orbium Caelestium* (Concerning the Revolutions of the Heavenly Spheres). 'Although Claudius Ptolemeus the Alexandrian, who in his admirable understanding and exactitude far surpasses the others, with the help of more than four-hundred-years-old observations brought this science almost to its perfection, so that nothing seemed to remain that he had not touched upon; yet we see many things which do not tally with what should have taken place according to his theory, and this is because certain other motions were discovered later that were unknown to him'.

Here he seems to be registering directly the great impression made on him in his youth by Novara's redetermination of the positions of Ptolemy's stars and his discovery of the changed aspect of the heavens. The contrast between Ptolemy's positions and those observed by Novara must have given him the keenest awareness of the differences which had accumulated during the preceding thirteen centuries.

Copernicus was conscious of the comparison between himself and Ptolemy. He regretted that his own situation for making astronomical observations had been so much less good than that of the ancient master whom he revered. ' Fortune did not give me, as it gave Claudius Ptolemy, that beautiful opportunity of experience. For him the skies were more cheerful, where the Nile does not breathe fogs as does our Vistula.' During thirty years' observations at Frauenburg, he did not once succeed in observing the planet Mercury, owing to the climate and the high latitude. This was a serious hindrance, for the elucidation of the irregularities of its motion was very important for his theory, and caused him 'much toil and effort'.

Copernicus quoted various problems, including that of the solar year, upon which opinions differed. Owing to the contradictions, many astronomers despaired of ever solving them exactly. But he would not conceal his fear of work under the pretext of the insuperability of these difficulties. For 'the number of auxiliary means for the study of the heavens is increasing with the passage of time and with our distance from the founders of this science. What I have recently discovered can be compared with their discoveries. Finally I admit openly that I teach many things differently from my predecessors, although we owe them a great debt for having been the first to undertake these investigations'.

Copernicus' bold and clear language, and his understanding of his own place in history, are very remarkable.

He described in the dedication of his book to Pope Paul III how he sought in the classics for a unifying idea by which order might be restored in the astronomical chaos. He was first struck by a passage in Cicero, where it was reported that Hicetas believed that 'the earth was moved' (Copernicus always referred to Hicetas as Nicetas). Then later he discovered in Plutarch that others had held the same opinion. He was particularly impressed by this passage, which he quotes: 'But while some say the earth stands still, Philolaus the Pythagorean held that it is moved about the element of fire in an oblique circle, after the same manner of motion that the sun and moon have. Heraclides of Pontus and Ecphantus the Pythagorean assign a motion to the earth, not progressive, but after the manner of a wheel being carried on its own axis. Thus the earth, they say, turns itself upon its own centre from West to East'.

'When from this, therefore', wrote Copernicus, 'I had conceived its possibility I myself also began to meditate upon the mobility of the earth. And although the opinion seemed absurd, yet because I knew the liberty had been accorded to others before me of imagining whatsoever circles they pleased to explain the phenomena of the stars, I thought I also might readily be allowed to experiment whether, by supposing the earth to have some motion, stronger demonstrations than those of the others could be found as to the revolution of the celestial sphere.'

Then he says that he 'found at length by much and long observation', that 'if the motions of the other planets were added to the rotation of the earth and calculated as for the revolution of that planet, not only the phenomena of the others followed from this, but also it so bound together both the order and magnitude of all the planets and the spheres and the heaven itself, that in no single part could one thing be altered without confusion among the other parts and in the universe.'

Copernicus does not say that the idea that the earth might go round the sun was his own invention. That would not have been true, and it might have been regarded as heretical and dangerous. So he carefully resurrected the idea from the ancients, and left the responsibility of suggesting it on them.

He forestalled opposition based on sacred literature with equal care, and extraordinary boldness. Let no one depend, he says, on the quotation of 'some place in the Scriptures wickedly distorted to their purpose'. Nor let them seek authority in Lactantius, who had derided those who had declared that the earth has the shape of a sphere. Lactantius was 'celebrated in other ways but very little in mathematics', and, says Copernicus, 'Mathematics is written for mathematicians'.

Copernicus's putting of this Father of the Church in his place to Paul III, who had just refounded the Inquisition, was a demonstration of his own intellectual courage. It showed, too, that the modern idea of the independent authority of science had arisen in his mind. And it was evidence also that a loyal churchman could still speak with striking intellectual freedom, and that the persecution of the new science by the church had not yet proceeded very far.

Copernicus explains that his astronomical labours may contribute something to the needs of the Church, for more accurate knowledge of the length of the year and the month, and the movements of the sun and moon was necessary in order to improve the calendar. He thus gave indirectly the reason why he had not accepted the invitation of Pope Leo X in 1514 to join his commission for the reform of the calendar: the requisite astronomical data were not yet available.

Besides dedicating his work to the Pope in order to secure protection against calumniators, Copernicus also wished to arouse interest in it. Paul III was a keen astrologer, who always consulted the stars before fixing the date of any function. Copernicus' ideas were received with respect by the Church for half a century after their first publication. Aggressive hostility to them grew rather slowly, and became violent in Protestant earlier than in Catholic circles.

Luther referred to Copernicus in one of his after-dinner speeches as that 'new astrologer who wanted to prove that the earth was moving and revolving, rather than the heaven or the firmament, sun and moon, just as if someone in a moving carriage or on a sailing ship believed that he was motionless and in rest, but that the earth and the trees were moving. But such are the times we live in : he who wants to be clever must invent something all his own and what he makes up he naturally thinks is the best thing ever! This fool wants to turn the whole art of astronomy upside down! But as the Holy Scripture testifies, Joshua ordered the sun to stand still, and not the earth!'

While Luther said such things of Copernicus, there is no record of any comment by Copernicus on the whole movement of the Reformation, and its leading figures.

Melanchthon described Copernicus' theory as 'an old joke', implying that it was a superfluous revival of a frivolous suggestion by Aristarchus of Samos. Calvin was no less obscurantist than Luther and Melanchthon. He quoted Psalm 93 against Copernicus : 'The world also is established, that it cannot be moved'.

There was even some popular ridicule of the theory in anti-catholic demonstrations. At Elbing, three miles from Frauenburg, the townspeople held carnivals, in which an actor, wearing the robes of a pope and accompanied by drunkards and knaves, rode in procession through the streets. In one of these processions, a townsman dressed in the garb of a canon mimicked Copernicus. The first head-master of the Elbing grammar school, an unorthodox Dutchman named Gnapheus who had been compelled to flee from Holland, wrote a burlesque in which a man touched the earth with the tip of his finger, and sent it reeling through space like a dancing goddess. It was performed in Elbing by the townspeople just before Copernicus' sixtieth birthday.

Nevertheless, Copernicus' first important disciple was a young Protestant professor from Wittenberg. This was Georg Joachim von Lauchen, who was born at Feldkirch in Austria, and took the Latin name of Rheticus. Melanchthon advised him to study mathematics, and had him appointed professor at the age of twenty-two. He became a great master of trigonometry, and compiled trigonometrical tables which are the basis of those still in use.

Rheticus had heard the rumours of Copernicus' new theories, and unlike his famous Wittenberg patrons, wished to know more about them. He obtained leave to visit Poland, and set out on his journey in April 1539. He was then twenty-five years old. He arrived at Frauenburg in May, uninvited and unannounced. Rheticus had come from the very heart of the Lutheran movement, and the reading of Lutheran literature had just been banned in Varmia.

The serene and learned Copernicus, now sixty-six years old, received him like a son. These independent and courageous men, the young and the old, coming from the two opposed religions, found perfect mutual understanding in science.

Rheticus threw himself with all his youthful intellectual enthusiasm into the study of the new theory. Within ten weeks he had substantially mastered it. He then had a slight illness, and Copernicus' friend Tiedemann Giese, Bishop of Kulm, invited them to stay for a rest in the country, at Löbau.

We can imagine the long quiet days of discussion between the old and the young man, of Copernicus' delight in finding someone who understood him, and Rheticus' youthful thrill at having the new conceptions of the future unfolded to him. Rheticus wrote a brilliant summary of the new theory for the information of the learned world, which he entitled the *Narratio Prima*, or first account.

In it he said that Copernicus ' was social by nature ' and saw that the scientific world stood in need of an improved system of astronomy. He had yielded to the entreaties of his old and learned friend, Bishop Giese, to prepare new astronomical tables, with a set of rules for their use. But he proposed not to publish the new theory on which they were based. Giese protested against this tactic of ·making users learn from experience the practical advantage of the new rules, before acquainting them with the theory on which they were based. He compared it with the political manoeuvre by which governments secretly put plans into operation in order to show their good results, before asking their subjects to approve them.

Rheticus, the Protestant, carefully emphasized the rôle of Giese, the Catholic, in persuading Copernicus to publish his controversial theory.

Rheticus said that his examination of Copernicus' work had convinced him that he was not inferior to Regiomontanus in mastery of astronomy, and in fact was more to be compared with Ptolemy, because he shared ' with Ptolemy the good fortune of completing, with the aid of divine kindness, the reconstruction of astronomy which he began, while Regiomontanus—alas, cruel fate—departed this life before he had time to erect his columns '.

He did not mention Copernicus by his surname, nor give his own in full, no doubt in order to avoid having their names too closely identified with the theory. Rheticus explained that Copernicus attributed the greatest importance to following the ancients. But when he became aware that the phenomena, and mathematics, compelled him to make certain assumptions, even against his wishes, he continued to aim his arrows at the same target as Ptolemy, but turned to weapons of a very different type. Copernicus abhorred anything that was alien to any honest man, particularly of a philosophic nature. He was far from thinking that he should depart from ancient ideas, except for good reasons. Such was his age, his seriousness of character and distinction in learning, his loftiness of spirit and greatness of mind, that no trifling speculation could take hold of him.

Rheticus commented that he had learned from his own studies of Regiomontanus the immense difficulty of providing a satisfactory new theory of astronomy. But after reading and witnessing the work which Copernicus had performed with such energy of mind, he realized that previously he had not even dreamt of the magnitude of the labour that was required, and was now almost completed.

He remarked that Copernicus always had before his eyes the observations of all ages, together with his own, assembled in order as in catalogues. Then, when some conclusion must be drawn, he proceeded from the earliest observations to his own, seeking the mutual relationship which harmonized them all.

The *First Account* was published as a pamphlet, and copies were sent to eminent learned persons. It stimulated interest in Copernicus' ideas, and increased the demand for their full publication, though it also brought forth some bitter comments, especially from Melanchthon. After he had read his copy, he said that some people thought it 'a distinguished achievement to construct such a crazy thing as that Prussian astronomer who moves the earth and fixes the sun. Verily, wise rulers should tame the unrestraint of men's minds '.

Copernicus said that one of the reasons why he had not acceded to the requests of his friends to publish a complete account of his work earlier, was the thought of the scorn which he had to fear on account of the novelty and incongruity of his theory. This well-nigh induced him to abandon the preparation of his treatise, which he had pursued 'not for nine years only, but to a fourth period of nine years'. In fact, he worked over and over his manuscript for nearly thirty-six years.

Copernicus had a very remarkable combination of bold thought with critical judgment. He wrote only one scientific book, into which he distilled the whole of his scientific life. He seems to have formulated his ideas in Italy, and then worked them out in the intellectual quiet and ecclesiastical security of his last thirty years at Frauenburg.

In the end, there was a danger that his criticism and caution would overcome his initiative, and that he would leave his masterpiece unpublished. But what his old and eminent friends had failed to do was accomplished by young Rheticus. After his pamphlet had raised the interest of the learned world in Copernicus' theory he offered to help with the publication, if Copernicus would complete the material. He found a publisher in Nuremberg, managed all the business details, and assisted with the correction of the proofs.

Rheticus stayed with Copernicus for no less than two years, helping the old astronomer in every practical way. The collaboration between the young enthusiast and the great old natural philosopher was one of the most touching and fortunate in the history of science. It was paralleled more than one hundred years later, when the young Edmund Halley persuaded Isaac Newton to write and publish his *Principia*, and bore the labour of seeing it through the press, and even paid for the printing.

With Rheticus at his side, egging him on, Copernicus completed the manuscript. The original still exists, having been found in a library in Prague after being lost for centuries. It is neatly written in Latin script, on small sheets of paper. Titles and initial words are written in red ink. There are numerous alterations, which show how in the course of years Copernicus gradually developed his ideas.

When his manuscript was completed, Copernicus wrote his magnificent dedication to Pope Paul III, explaining his position with much clarity and forthrightness.

However, the final stages of publication were not without difficulty. The Lutheran publisher in Nuremberg took fright over the radical scientific opinions in the book, and engaged Osiander, the local Lutheran priest, to write an unsigned diplomatic foreword, in which Copernicus' theory is described as a mere hypothesis, which simplified the calculations, and did not necessarily imply that the revolution of the earth round the sun was real.

When Copernicus read it, he was profoundly shocked. It contradicted the very essence of his conception that the revolutions of the planets round the sun were real. It implied, according to Copernicus' outlook, that science could not in fact discover anything real about the external world.

About this time Copernicus, who was now sixty-nine, had a severe stroke. It has been suggested that this was caused by Osiander's foreword. He sickened seriously, and presently lost his intellectual vigour and memory.

Tiedemann Giese wrote to their common friend Donner that, as even in his days of good health he had always been habitually retiring, now that he was seriously ill probably only a few friends would stand sympathetically at his bedside. He therefore begged him to give all brotherly care to the man that both of them had always loved, so that he would not be solitary in his affliction, for 'we are all his debtors on account of his pure soul, his integrity, and his extensive learning'.

At the beginning of May 1543, the final printing of his

book was hurried on, and a copy of the finished work was put into his hands on May 27th. His comprehension had probably already gone, and an hour or so later, he died.

Copernicus was buried beside his uncle Watzelrode in the Frauenburg cathedral.

His book was well-received by Pope Paul III. The subsequent attacks on it arose from the general struggle of the Church against Protestantism. It was not put on the papal Index of banned books until 1616. Paul III was himself the leader of the counter-reformation, which was marked by his authorization of the order of the Jesuits in 1540, and the re-establishment of the Holy Inquisition in 1542. These institutions were not used against the book he welcomed until after his time. He did not regard them as instruments against science but against disorder in religion. It was he who excommunicated Henry VIII, and severed England from the Catholic family.

Though one of the very greatest works of the human mind, Copernicus' treatise never became popular. Even after five centuries, only four editions have appeared, and it has not yet been completely translated into English.

The reason for this is that the book was mainly concerned with the establishment of an idea of supreme importance. It achieved this aim with an overwhelming and final completeness. But it was not an elementary primer, or textbook for instruction in the practical rules for utilizing astronomical observations. The pre-Copernican textbooks continued to go through many editions after the *Revolutions* had been published, because practical men were more familiar with the old rules. They were not very much interested in the conceptions on which the subject was based, but only in making quick calculations for practical purposes in navigation and astrology.

Copernicus was not particularly good at technical matters. He made many mistakes in calculations, showing that he had no special skill as a computer. He did not use the very latest methods of his day in mathematics. He was not more than ordinarily competent in making astronomical observations. He did not use the best obtainable instruments. He devised ingenious ones of his own, made out of sticks and bits of metal, which were crude, but sufficient for his purpose. One of these instruments subsequently came into the hands of Tycho Brahe, who marvelled at what Copernicus had got out of it. As an observer, Copernicus was about twenty times less accurate than Tycho Brahe. He was not interested in measurement for its own sake, but only as a means for deciding theoretical questions.

His work was completely convincing only to men of ideas, and was not sufficiently precise to satisfy the mere technicians. Copernicus did not give a very accurate description of the movements of the planets because he assumed that they revolved in perfect circles. He was strongly impressed by the ancient metaphysical idea that the circle, as the perfect curve, is the natural form of movement for a celestial body. In fact, the planets revolve not in perfect circles but in very round ellipses. Until Kepler had discovered this, and worked out the details, the Copernican system did not give practical results which were more accurate than the old system.

The popularization of his conception needed something much more concrete than the logic of the scientific imagination. This came with Galileo's introduction of the telescope, which enabled the ordinary man to see a multitude of new sights in the heavens that were a direct confirmation of the Copernican system. The new ' optic glass ' was as exciting to the people of Galileo's day as television is to ours. Through it they could see the moons circulating round Jupiter, like the planets round the sun.

For Copernicus himself, Rheticus, Kepler, Galileo and a few others, such concrete demonstrations were not necessary. If Copernicus had lived to see the invention of the telescope, he would have looked at the heavens with intense interest, but he would not have been astonished by what he saw. For him, the logic of science was paramount and enough. It had already prepared his imagination for what he would have seen.

In addition to the primary idea of the demonstration of the revolution of the planets round the sun, Copernicus developed other very important ideas. He pointed out that the fact that the movement of the earth round the sun did not alter the positions of the fixed stars, as they appeared to an observer on the earth, implied that the stars must be very far away. 'What follows from this demonstration,' he says, 'is that the heavens are infinite, in relation to the earth. The extent of this immensity we do not know at all.'

Copernicus was the first to give mankind a true insight into the magnitude of the universe. In his discussion of whether the earth moved round the sun, or *vice versa*, he showed a strong and clear understanding of the relativity of motion. 'For every apparent change of position is due, either to a motion of the object observed, or to the motion of the observer, or to unequal changes in the positions of both.' These words have a very modern ring.

Ptolemy's chief arguments against the rotation of the earth on its axis had been physical. He thought that if this were so, then the clouds, unattached to the earth, would drift from east to west, as it whirled round beneath them. Copernicus considered that the clouds would be held to the earth by gravitation. 'I consider gravity as nothing but a natural striving with which the Creator has endowed the parts in order that they may combine into one *whole* while they collect into a sphere. The same is probably true of the sun, the moon and the other planets, and yet they are not fixed.'

Here Newton's theory of gravitation is foreshadowed, and the basic principle of modern cosmology, which supposes that the stars and planets are formed by the condensation of nebulous matter and dust into spheres, through the mutual forces of gravitational attraction between the constituent particles.

Copernicus quoted the roundness of a water-drop as an example of matter collecting together in the shape of a sphere, through the inter-action of its internal forces, and it was characteristic of his imagination to extend this idea to celestial bodies, and the whole universe.

Another of Ptolemy's arguments against the rotation of the earth was that it would fly to pieces under centrifugal force. Copernicus countered this by pointing out that, as the universe is immensely larger than the earth, then, if it rotated, the centrifugal forces generated in it would be enormously greater than those in the rotating earth. In fact, a rotating universe was much more likely to fly to pieces under centrifugal forces than a rotating earth.

Copernicus noticed that the ancient astronomers tended to make their observations fit a pre-conceived theory. This led him to recognize the great importance of the personal equation in observation, and to take precautions to prevent pre-conceived ideas from unconsciously affecting the result.

There are several resemblances between Copernicus and Newton. Both of them produced a system of nature. Both worked for long years in isolation, and completed their ideas without proposing to publish them. Newton's secrecy was perhaps more neurotic than Copernicus', for in his day, there was no serious danger in being accused of scientific heresies.

Copernicus' retreat at Frauenburg had a certain resemblance to Newton's at Cambridge. Both were in the learned world, and yet sufficiently far from the centre of things to have plenty of quiet for thought and reflection. Frauenburg was a good place to reflect on the lessons of Bologna and Rome, just as Cambridge was a good place for reflecting on the scientific news from London, Paris, and the world.

Both Copernicus and Newton had considerable experience in affairs. Both had participated in parliaments, and had been concerned with questions of currency and finance. Both were scholarly bachelors.

All the portraits of Copernicus depict him with a bold and direct gaze. He looks a strong character, but habitually withdrawn into his own inner reflections. Unlike many scholars, however, he shows no sign of fear of the outer world. Some of his portraits give his mouth a slight twist, which has been interpreted as a sign of harshness. It was more probably an unconscious expression of stubborn determination, not to be persuaded against his better conviction. He must have spent a great deal of nervous energy in supporting his conviction that the earth went round the sun, against the universal opinion of mankind and history.

Altogether, Copernicus is revealed as a very great man. In the midst of a busy life of affairs, he quietly elaborated his revolutionary system of the world, through forty years of private labour, reading, collecting data, observing, calculating, and revising his work over and over again. He was a whole man, and a healthy character. He liked to retire and reflect, but he was 'social by nature'. He was the reverse of neurotic.

He was content to allow his work to take its course without very anxious concern, because he had a solid character and social position. He had a just appreciation of its value, and was confident of the verdict of posterity. He did not care very much whether recognition came sooner or later.

He was a product of the liberal side of the Catholic

Church. He had many friends among the learned humanist bishops. He had absorbed everything which this spirit could give. But without participating in the Reformation, he had the realism which was its deepest quality. He collaborated with the Protestant Rheticus just as easily as with his old Catholic friends. He may have inherited his realistic spirit from his native land beside the Baltic.

He seemed to combine in himself the best qualities of the Church and the Reformation. He was born in Poland, educated in Italy, a child of the Renaissance and a parent of the modern world.

REFERENCES

Copernicus and his World, by H. Kesten. Secker & Warburg : 1945.

Three Copernican Treatises, Translated with Introduction and Notes by E. Rosen. Columbia University Press : 1939.

Nicolaus Copernicus: De Revolutionibus. Preface and Book I, translated by J. F. Dobson and S. Brodetsky. Royal Astronomical Society : 1947.

GALILEO GALILEI
1564 - 1642

GALILEO was the first modern scientist. His works are the earliest in which the scientific reader of today feels quite at home. He was the first to work out the scientific method completely. He invented physics, and made Copernicus' imaginings concrete.

The moral problems in which he was involved through the conflicts of science and religion are not unlike those which face the scientist of today regarding his responsibility for the discovery and use of atomic energy.

The very years of Galileo's birth and death are significant of modern times. He was born in the same year as Shakespeare, and died in the year that Newton was born. He links them together in time, and was their peer in ability.

Galileo Galilei was born in Pisa on February 15th, 1564. His father, Vincenzio, was descended from one of the leading families in Florence, which had provided fourteen of the chief officers of the city during the two preceding centuries. By Vincenzio's time, however, the family fortunes had declined. He was a talented musician, an authority on counter-point, and wrote important works on music, but he was impelled through lack of means to support himself by business. In 1581 he published his *Dialogue on Ancient and Modern Music*, which exhibited great knowledge and laborious research. He was an exquisite performer on the lute, and remarked that the best of these instruments at that time were made in England. He knew Latin and Greek, and was a skilful mathematician.

More than all this, he was an outspoken supporter of free intellectual enquiry. In his *Dialogue* he says: ' It appears to me that they who in proof of any assertion rely simply on the weight of authority, without adducing any argument in support of it, act very absurdly. I, on the contrary, wish to be allowed freely to question and freely to answer without any sort of adulation, as well becomes those who are sincerely in search of truth '.

Galileo might have taken this saying as the motto of his life, for it is the perfect expression of the best aspect of his spirit, and it seems fair to conclude that he owed much to his father for his intellectual attitude.

Vincenzio Galilei had seven children, three of them sons, of whom Galileo was the eldest. He was not a successful man. He spent much time in travel, trying to make a living, and left his family in lodgings in Pisa. Galileo spent his childhood in this town. He received some schooling, and his father helped him with Greek and Latin.

When he was about twelve, he was sent to the Jesuit monastery at Vallombrosa, near Florence, where he received a good training in Latin and Greek. Milton visited this beautiful place, built in a thickly-wooded valley, and invoked his memory of the banks of fallen leaves in his description in *Paradise Lost* of Satan's prostrate followers:

His legions, angel forms who lay entranced,
Thick as autumnal leaves that strow the banks
In Vallombrosa, where the Etrurian shades
High over-arched imbower . . .

The Jesuits made much progress with their quick-minded pupil, who intimated to his father that he would like to become a novice. This was not at all to Vincenzio Galilei's taste. As he had no property, he wished his son to become a cloth-dealer, one of the most prosperous Florence trades. It happened that Galileo had an attack of ophthalmia, so his father made this an excuse for removing him from the monastery.

From his boyhood, Galileo showed remarkable manual as well as mental aptitude. Like many boys, he was very fond of making things, and not all of his models worked. He played the lute beautifully, and was a creditable organist. He had great skill in drawing and painting, and used to say in later life that if he had been free to choose his profession, he would have become a painter.

He was fond of poetry in his youth, and had a very strong memory for his favourite authors. He could recite whole works of Virgil, Horace, Seneca, Petrarch and Ariosto. His first known lecture to an academy was a piece of literary criticism on Dante, in which he discussed the site and dimensions of the *Inferno*.

When Vincenzio Galilei saw the signs of extraordinary powers, he decided that his son would be more suited to a scientific profession than a business. He sent him to study medicine at the university of Pisa, which he entered in 1581, when he was seventeen. His father tried for three years to secure a scholarship for him, but failed. His chief professor was Andrea Cesalpino, the distinguished physician and botanist.

From the first, Galileo showed himself disputatious. The custom in those days was for students to listen in profound deference to their professors, but Galileo argued about everything on its merits. He attended the lectures on Aristotle's scientific works, and made careful notes, which still exist, of their substance. He was not content to learn what was said, but independently discussed its meaning. Though he always spoke with respect of Aristotle himself, he was quite without reverence for the exaggerated authority accorded to him, and contradicted his views when they seemed to him wrong. This was regarded as bordering on blasphemy.

He was nicknamed the 'Wrangler', and engendered hostility as a turbulent intellectual from the beginning of his student days. It seems that he was doing nothing more than carrying into practice the freely-enquiring spirit of his father. But being endowed with almost unparalleled intellectual strength and energy, he swiftly produced a profound disturbance.

He made his first famous discovery a few months after he had entered the university, when he was eighteen. As with many other students, his mind was apt to wander while at service in chapel, and one day his eye fell upon a swinging lamp. He noticed that the time of the swing seemed to be independent of the width of the swing. When he got home he experimented with a bullet tied on the end of a piece of string. He gathered up the string into his hand, until the time of the swing of the bullet coincided with his pulse, and he found that as the swing died down its time continued to coincide with his pulse. In this way he proved that the time of swing was independent of its amplitude, and thereby invented the pendulum.

Vincenzio Galilei, though a good mathematician, had not taught his son mathematics, as he considered it would distract him from his medical studies. Galileo did not become interested in mathematics until his second year at Pisa, and then by accident. It was the custom for the Medicean Court to reside at Pisa during the winter. With the court were the Grand Duke's pages, whose education was supervised by a tutor named Ricci, who was a capable mathematician. Galileo became friendly with Ricci, and happened one day to visit him when he was giving his pupils a lesson in Euclid.

He watched Ricci's demonstrations and the fascination of geometry suddenly seized him, as it has many talented youths throughout the centuries, and Galileo immediately raced through the subject with all his genius.

His father had lately moved from Pisa to Florence, but he was still as unprosperous as ever. He could not afford to keep his son at the university any longer, so Galileo left the university after four years, without taking a degree. He went to Florence to live with the family, and he renewed his studies with Ricci. These led him to the works of Archimedes, which inspired in him the full vision of the nature of physical science.

Archimedes had shown that King Hiero's crown was not made of pure gold, because it had a larger volume than an equal weight of pure gold. He proved this by putting the crown and the equivalent weight of gold into separate vessels of water each full to the brim. The crown caused more water to overflow than the lump of pure gold. From this, Archimedes made an analysis of the mechanics of liquids in which he used mathematics to describe their properties.

Galileo learned from Archimedes how to combine mathematics with experiments in order to elucidate the properties of matter. He saw that this was the essence of the science of physics, and by clearly recognizing and announcing this principle, he became the founder of modern physics.

Following on his study of Archimedes, Galileo invented a balance by which the relative weights of the constituents in an alloy of two metals could be directly measured. His experiments were remarkably accurate and his measurements of the specific gravities of substances agree very closely with modern figures.

This work, and his invention of the pendulum, attracted the attention of the mathematical nobleman, Guidobaldo del Monte, who corresponded with him, and recommended him to the Grand Duke of Tuscany, Ferdinando I, as a young man of great talent.

Galileo had not yet obtained a regular source of income. He earned a little by coaching pupils, and tried to obtain a professorship. Even with the high notice he had already achieved, he was turned down by five universities, Bologna, Rome, Padua, Pisa and Florence, in his first attempts to obtain a chair. He had begun to think of emigrating to the East, when, in 1589, the chair of mathematics at Pisa again fell vacant. This time, Guidobaldo and his brother Cardinal del Monte ensured that Galileo was appointed. He was then twenty-five years old. The salary was very low; only about 60 scudi a year. The salary for the chair of medicine was 2000 scudi a year, showing the low estimation in which mathematics was held.

At Pisa, Galileo continued his Archimedean experiments, with investigations of the centre of gravity of bodies. He discovered the curve known as the cycloid. This is the path traced out by a particle of dust on the rim of a wheel rolling along the ground. It makes a graceful arch, and following Galileo's suggestion, a new bridge over the river Arno, the Ponte di Mezzo, was built with arches of this shape.

As a professor he now had the opportunity to pursue in a systematic way his questioning of the physical science of Aristotle, which previously he had been able to do, in the main, only by logical arguing in the lecture-room.

Aristotle had laid down that bodies fell with a speed proportional to their weight. It is said that Galileo disproved this assertion by dropping two bodies of different weights from the top of the Leaning Tower of Pisa, before a large concourse of people, who saw that both of them struck the ground at the same moment.

There is no good evidence for this story, and in any case, the Dutch scientist Simon Stevin had already performed this kind of experiment convincingly. Galileo's investigation was far more comprehensive. As freely falling bodies fall so fast, he devised a way of slowing them down in a controlled manner, so that it became possible to measure exactly what was happening. He assumed that a metal ball rolling down an inclined plane would follow the same law, but at a reduced speed.

He obtained a straight 'piece of wood moulding or scantling', about eighteen feet long and nine inches wide, and 'three finger-breadths' thick. He cut a channel 'a little more than one finger in breadth' on the edge. He made it 'very straight, smooth and polished', and lined it with parchment. Then he propped one end of the wood from one to three feet higher than the other, so that it made an inclined plane. Down the groove he rolled a 'hard, smooth, and very round ball', and measured the time it took to roll various distances, with such accuracy that the difference between two measurements never exceeded 'one tenth of a pulse beat'.

This was done by opening and closing the little spout of a water-clock with his finger, and weighing the amount of water that had run out during the interval. He made a series of marks along the groove, and carefully measured the time taken by the ball to roll the distances between them. He repeated each experiment many times, to be quite sure that he always got the same result, within the limits of the accuracy of his experimental method. So he discovered the precise relations between the distance, time and speed of the ball's motion on the inclined plane. From the exact data on how the rate of motion of the ball increased as it passed successive marks, he arrived at the notion of *acceleration*, i.e., the rate of change of velocity.

He discussed what would happen to a ball which was

started with a given speed, rolling *up* an inclined plane. He saw that if the slope of the plane was very small, the ball would lose its speed very slowly, and if the plane were quite level and there were no friction, the ball would presumably go on for ever, with the speed at which it was originally started. He had arrived at the idea of *inertia*.

Thus Galileo discovered the principles of the science of the motion of bodies. The ground was now clear for Newton to invent the mathematical technique for dealing with them, and build the main structure of modern physical science.

Galileo wrote an extensive account of his researches on motion in 1590, when he was twenty-six years old, and still at Pisa. His original notes were not published as he made them until two centuries after his death, but he worked them over and over during his life, and expounded them with supreme elegance in his *Dialogue on Two New Sciences*, published in 1638.

As he got each new result at Pisa, he immediately spoke of it in his university lectures, exposing with devastating sarcasm and brilliant proof the shortcomings of Aristotelian physics. His colleagues heard these discourses with mounting irritation.

Presently, they were able to get their own back. Giovanni Medici, the illegitimate son of Cosimo I, had designed a gigantic dredger for clearing Leghorn harbour. Galileo was asked to examine the model, and reported that it would not work. Nevertheless, the dredger was made, and failed. Giovanni was annoyed. He joined the Aristotelian opposition to Galileo. Hisses and disturbances occurred in his lectures, and by 1592 he was forced to resign his chair.

In these early years at Pisa, when he was laying the foundations of modern physics, he was also active in literature. He composed a severe critique of Tasso for the Florence Academy, in which he described his poetry as 'pap for cats'.

He passionately admired Ariosto, whose *Orlando Furioso* he knew by heart. Reading Tasso after Ariosto was like eating 'cucumbers after melons'.

He drafted a prose comedy, a 'somewhat licentious burlesque', in which he ridiculed the university rules concerning the wearing of gowns. It hastened his departure from the University of Pisa, and earned him the reputation of being a man of easy morals, and unmindful of professorial dignity.

From time to time he wrote sonnets, and years later, one of these, on the telescope, was prefixed to Malatesti's volume of poems, entitled the *Sphinx*. When Milton visited Italy, he stayed with Malatesti, who presented him with a copy of this work.

Though Galileo's professorial salary at Pisa was only 60 scudi, he helped his relatives generously. His sister Virginia was married in 1591 to the son of an ambassador, and he felt he must give her a present which would uphold the family's honour. 'I am preparing for Virginia a set of silken bed-curtains, the silk for which I bought at Lucca, and have had it woven at little cost, so that, although the stuff is one and a quarter yards wide, it only cost me about three carlini the yard. The stuff is made with selvage, and will be sure to please. I am now having made the silk fringes for ornamenting the curtains, and could also have the bedstead made if desired. I beg you not to speak of this in the house, as I wish it to be an unexpected surprise. I will bring them at the Carnival holidays, and, if you wish, I could also bring enough to make four or five vests of damask and velvet of an exquisite design'.

Then, shortly afterwards, his father died. Galileo undertook to pay his sister's large dowry, and to support the rest of the family. Many years passed before he could complete the dowry payments to his brother-in-law, who at one time threatened him with imprisonment on account of the debt.

After he was forced to resign from Pisa, he returned to Florence, without a post, and with heavy family responsibilities. He now laid siege to the chair of mathematics at Padua, which had been vacant since 1588. He was supported by del Monte, who was an old student of Padua, and had influential relatives in the Venetian Republic, within which Padua was situated.

He set out for Padua at the end of the summer of 1592 with letters of introduction, and all his wordly goods in a box weighing less than 100 lb. After collecting more support in the university, he went on to Venice, to present his application to the authorities. He was successful against some strong competition, and returned to Florence to settle his affairs. He secured a visa from the Grand Duke of Tuscany to leave his native country and go to teach in the foreign republic.

The official announcement of his appointment still exists, and in it he is already described as 'the first in his profession', and his salary was fixed at 180 florins.

There followed eighteen years of intellectual activity which has not been surpassed by anyone in history. Galileo extended his researches in mechanics, and discovered the principle of virtual work, which underlies the popular maxim that what is gained in speed is lost in power. With the aid of this principle, all cases of mechanical equilibrium can be analyzed.

He invented the Sector, a calculating instrument which has been used ever since by engineers and military officers. It consists of two straight rulers hinged together at one end, so that they can be inclined at any angle, and be moved over a quadrant centred on the hinge. Various lines engraved on the surfaces of the rulers and quadrant facilitated a wide range of calculations. The sector could be used to calculate exchange rates in currency, and amounts of interest. It could be used to extract square and cube roots, find mean proportionals, and calculate the sizes of front and flank formations of armies. The equivalent of one solid could be found in another, which was useful in calculating the volume of fortifications, and estimating the quantity of materials and the amount of labour necessary for their construction.

It would give the change of weight of a body when transformed from one material into another, for example, the weight in silver of an exact replica of a gold crown. In addition, there were markings which assisted the drawing of many-sided regular figures, and lines by which the slope of a fortification could be measured.

He received orders from all over Europe for this device, and opened a workshop to manufacture it. Ultimately the sale ran into thousands.

In his workshop he made magnetic compasses and other instruments, and had at hand mechanics who could make any new apparatus that he devised for research.

He wrote treatises on military architecture, fortifications and mechanics which circulated widely in manuscript. Together with all his own original work, he gave conventional university lectures on astronomy, in which he expounded the ancient Ptolemaic system.

In 1597, Kepler, then twenty-five years old, sent him a copy of his first book, in which he supported the Copernican system. After reading the preface, Galileo wrote to him, thanking him for the gift and promising to read the rest of the book. 'This I shall do the more willingly because many years ago I became a convert to the opinions of Copernicus, and by his theory have succeeded in explaining many phenomena which on the contrary hypothesis are altogether inexplicable. I have arranged many arguments and confutations of the opposite opinions, which, however, I have not dared to publish, fearing the fate of our master, Copernicus, who, although he has earned immortal fame among a few, yet by an infinite number (for so only can the number of fools be measured) is hissed and derided. If there were many such as you I would venture to publish my speculations, but since that is not so I shall take time to consider it'.

To this the youthful Kepler replied : ' What advantage is there in deceit? Have faith Galileo, and go forward. If I am right, few of the foremost mathematicians of Europe will wish to secede from us: such is the power of truth. If Italy is less favourable for publication and if you are likely to have other obstacles, perhaps Germany will concede us this liberty . . .'

Galileo never answered this letter. Though Kepler fully appreciated his genius, Galileo always remained cool to Kepler's. Galileo was at heart a laboratory experimental physicist, whereas Kepler was at heart an astronomer. In later years Galileo said of Kepler : 'His manner of philosophizing is not mine'. Besides the difference in their fundamental scientific interests, their Italian and German social and cultural backgrounds were in deep contrast. Galileo always felt that Kepler was alien to him.

The first six years' period of Galileo's appointment as professor ended in 1598. The Venetian authorities were slow to renew it, as it was customary for the salary to be raised. After much pressure, they agreed to another six years at 320 florins a year. He was told not to expect any further rise for the Venetian 'Senate did not choose to make his case a precedent for every learned and hungry foreigner who might think fit to press a similar claim'.

Students were now flocking from all over Europe to hear him. Among them were Ferdinand, the future Emperor of Germany, and other princes. He moved into a large

house, where many of his distinguished students became
lodgers.

William Harvey studied in Padua from 1598–1602, and
would have heard his lectures. No doubt the widespread
discussions of Galileo's revolutionary discoveries on motion,
and the properties of liquids and pumps, directed his mind
to find the explanation of the working of the heart in the
terms of motion, and thus led him to the discovery of the
circulation of the blood.

Galileo had about twenty student lodgers. He superin-
tended the catering himself. He was a great connoisseur of
food and wine, and no mean hand at cooking. He was far
too much interested in the table, and that everyone should
enjoy themselves so that the conversation should be good,
to bother about accounts, and he made no profit out of his
housekeeping.

Even in his old age, when he was infirm and prodigiously
distinguished, he cooked delicacies to send to his daughter
in a Franciscan convent. She in turn sent the convent clock
to him to repair, which he did, but not with permanent
success, as she subsequently reported to him.

Galileo's extraordinary combination of intellectual and
manual skill was reminiscent of Leonardo da Vinci. In this
he was a late flower of the Italian Renaissance.

He spent much time in his large garden, weeding, pruning
and cultivating vines. He liked to discourse on all the things
happening in it to friends and pupils, as they stood around.
It seemed to help him to turn ideas over in his mind. He
illustrated his lectures by all kinds of homely phenomena
he observed at hand. His audiences grew until the great hall
of the university, which held a thousand, was not always
large enough, and he had to adjourn to speak in the open
air.

On summer evenings he had supper in his garden, beneath the vine trellises. He never ate alone if he could avoid it, and passionately loved intelligent discussion. At these parties he entertained his friends, and soothed himself, by playing the lute. It is not surprizing to learn that Galileo was a great admirer of Plato's literary art, and wrote his chief works in the form of dialogues, which stand beside Plato's own in greatness. In his later less fortunate years, Galileo often recalled the beautiful past at Padua; 'Quel beato tempo di Padova' he used to say.

The appearance of the brilliant new star of 1604 (a super-nova) increased his attention to astronomy. He spoke on the new star to immense audiences, pointing out that as it remained fixed with regard to the other stars when viewed at different times of the year, (that is, it showed no parallax) it must be very distant.

The appearance of this new star had great philosophical importance, for it was cited as evidence against the Aristotelian view that the heavens were perfect and unchangeable. Here was a star which was new and which changed in brightness. After the blow to the old theory, Galileo came out publicly in favour of the Copernican system.

His appointment to the chair was renewed, with a salary increased to 520 florins. At this period he became interested in William Gilbert's treatise *On Magnetism*, the first great modern English book on science. Gilbert had made magnificent experiments in which he had shown that the magnetic properties of the earth could be imitated in the laboratory with a magnetized sphere. Galileo found Gilbert's assertion that the earth and moon attract each other like two magnets very suggestive. It substituted a concrete physical force of known character for a vague mystical influence, and laid the foundation for the subsequent conception of gravitation.

Galileo spoke more highly of Gilbert than of any other modern scientist. 'I extremely praise, admire, and envy this author. I think him, moreover, worthy of the greatest praise for the many new and true observations that he has made, to the disgrace of so many vain and fabling authors, who write, not from their own knowledge, but repeat everything they hear from the foolish vulgar, without attempting to satisfy themselves of the same by experiment—perhaps that they may not diminish the size of their books'.

Galileo returned home to Florence for the long summer vacation. He was engaged in 1601 as a holiday tutor by the Grand Duke, to coach his son Cosimo, who was then eleven years old, in mathematics. This brought him into close relations with the Medicis.

As the successful member of the family, his relatives looked to him for every kind of support. His brother Michelangelo demanded that he should find him a job. He was a lute-player, with elegant manners. Galileo secured a post for him in the court of a Polish prince. He would be dressed like the first gentleman in the court, he would be provided with two servants, a coach-and-four, and two hundred Hungarian ducats a year, with perquisites.

Galileo advanced the money for his journey, but received virtually nothing in return. Four years later Michelangelo was back in Padua, and Galileo secured for him the post of music master in the court of the Duke of Bavaria.

Meanwhile, he had been dunned on behalf of his sister Livia, who demanded to be married. Galileo found a gentleman of modest social rank who was prepared to marry her for a matter of 1800 ducats; 600 in ready cash and 200 for a trousseau were to be paid down, and the balance within five years. He guaranteed the settlement, hoping that Michelangelo would return some of the money he had lent him. But his brother had just got married, and had spent a large sum on the wedding banquet. In answer to Galileo's complaints that he sent nothing towards the dowries,

Michelangelo replied that he had to give a large party to keep up the custom of the country.

There were eighty guests, including no less than four ambassadors. He could never be accused of spending money for his own gratification. He had never thrown money away, and had, indeed, often denied himself in order to save. As to his sisters' dowries, Galileo should have given not only what he thought fit, but also what was in conformity with his brother's purse. 'But, good heavens! the idea of toiling all one's life just to put by a few farthings to give one's sisters! This joke would be indeed too heavy and bitter . . .' Finally, he was in great want of lutes, and if Galileo would send them more quickly he 'would not mind paying something more for the carriage'.

Besides supporting his father's family, Galileo now had one of his own. In 1599 a Venetian woman of the working class, Marina Gamba, became his mistress. They were never married, but they had three children, two girls and a boy. The eldest girl, Virginia, was born in 1600; the second, Livia, in 1601, and his son Vincenzio in 1606.

Galileo felt the ties of his relatives, and of his native country, Tuscany, very strongly. He felt himself to be a foreigner in the Venetian Republic, and always hoped that he would be able to settle down in Florence, the home of his ancestors. His attempts to achieve this were at first unsuccessful, and a remarkable event seemed to put an end to the aspiration.

In June 1609, he heard a rumour in Venice of the invention of the telescope in Holland. It at once set him thinking, and on the basis of his knowledge of optical perspective, he immediately designed and constructed one for himself. News of the wonders to be seen through it spread swiftly, and he was summoned by the Venetian Senate to demonstrate it to them.

'Many of the nobles and senators, although of a great age, mounted more than once to the top of the highest church tower in Venice, (the Campanile) in order to see sails and shipping that were so far off that it was two hours before they were seen, without my spy-glass, steering full sail into the harbour; for the effect of my instrument is such that it makes an object fifty miles off appear as large as if it were only five'.

The Doge perceived the naval and military value of the invention and desired to possess it, so Galileo presented it to him. His professorship at Padua was immediately confirmed for life, and his salary raised to 1000 florins a year.

He lamented to his brother-in-law that as 'Fortune's wings are swift but that those of Hope are drooping', with regard to his securing a post in Florence, he had accepted the offer, though it meant that he was bound to Padua for life, 'and can only hope to enjoy a sight of my own country during the recesses'.

Galileo very rapidly made new and improved telescopes. He demonstrated one to his former pupil Cosimo II, now Grand Duke of Tuscany, who was surprized and delighted to see with it that 'the moon was a body very similar to the earth'.

By January 1610 he had constructed a telescope which would magnify thirty times. A stream of astounding discoveries were presented to his eyes, which he described daily in his diary. He observed the mountains on the moon, and calculated their height from the length of their shadows, arriving at the figure of 4 or 5 miles, before the height of the great mountains on the earth had been measured.

He found that the Milky Way was not a scarf of nebulous cloud, but consisted of myriads of individual stars. He saw that Jupiter was a great globe, accompanied by four revolving moons, a whole planetary system in miniature.

He hastened to send an account to the Secretary of the Medicean Court, in which he gave 'thanks to God, who has been pleased to make me the first observer of marvellous things unrevealed to bygone ages'.

He wrote a pamphlet relating his discoveries day by day, and issued it in March 1610 under the title of *The Messenger of the Stars* (Siderus Nuncius). This pamphlet, with its rush of amazing discoveries within a few days, described in the most graphic style, produced the greatest sensation in the history of science. It opened a new window on the universe, and every man and woman could now see with their own eyes the things which Copernicus had imagined and inferred.

Such was Galileo's expository gift that his descriptions in the *Messenger* could have been published in a twentieth century newspaper virtually without editing. All that has been slowly and painfully learned about the technique of exposition of science to the public during the last three centuries, he already knew. He was indeed a forerunner of the modern man, and could have stepped straight into our own times without a qualm.

On the title-page of his *Messenger*, he described it as 'unfolding great and marvellous sights, and proposing them to the attention of everyone, but especially philosophers and astronomers, being such as have been observed by Galileo Galilei, a gentleman of Florence, professor of mathematics in the University of Padua, with the aid of a telescope lately invented by him'.

Galileo had not, in fact, invented the idea of the telescope, though he constructed the first good ones.

After expounding his discoveries about the moon, fixed stars and Milky Way, he proceeded to describe what he 'considered the most important in this work, namely that I should disclose and publish to the world the occasion of discovering and observing four *planets*, never seen from the very beginning of the world up to our own times . . . On the seventh of January in the present year, 1610, in the first hour of the following night, when I was viewing the constellations of the heavens through a telescope, the planet Jupiter presented itself to my view . . . and I noticed a circumstance which I had never been able to notice before, namely, that three little stars, small but very bright, were near the planet; and although I believed them to belong to the number of the fixed stars, yet they made me somewhat wonder, because they seemed to be arranged exactly in a straight line'. He introduced a little diagram of their positions which he had jotted down in his diary. But thinking they were fixed stars he scarcely bothered about them more, until, on the following night, January 8th, 'led by some fatality, I turned again to look at the same part of the heavens, I found a very different state of things'. He now saw three little stars to the west of Jupiter, whereas on the former night only one was on the west, and two were on the east side. His first fear was that Jupiter was not behaving itself, and that it was straying from the path among the stars calculated for it by the astronomers. He 'therefore waited for the next night with the most intense longing', but he was disappointed because is was cloudy. But on the nights of January 10th and 11th he had better luck. Comparisons of the new positions of the little stars caused him to conclude unhesitatingly, 'that there are three stars in the heavens moving about Jupiter, as Venus and Mercury round the sun'. On January 12th he observed yet a fourth satellite, and had further good seeing on the 13th, but on the 14th it was cloudy.

The discovery presented 'a notable and splendid argument to remove the scruples of those who can tolerate the revolution of the planets round the sun in the Copernican system ', but who thought that the existence of the earth's moon was in contradiction with that system.

Galileo received numerous demands for telescopes, and set up a shop to make them. He ground the lenses himself, and the quality of his instruments was not equalled elsewhere until the middle of the seventeenth century. During the first half of 1610 he produced more than one hundred telescopes, which were supplied with copies of his *Messenger* to numerous princes and learned men in Europe.

Galileo named the moons of Jupiter after the Medici family, as part of his siege to their favour. The Queen of France, Marié de Medici, of the same family, was jealous, and asked him that in case he discovered 'any other fine star, call it by the name of the Great Star of France '.

In Florence a public fête was organized in his honour, and in Venice there was a popular frenzy. Anyone seen peering through a telescope was liable to be mobbed.

The Aristotelian learned world was in consternation. They tried to evade the horrid novelties by refusing to see them. Galileo wrote to Kepler: 'What do you say of the leading philosophers here to whom I have offered a thousand times, of my own accord, to show my studies, but who, with the lazy obstinacy of a serpent who has eaten his fill, have never consented to look at the planets, or moon, or telescope? Verily, just as serpents close their ears, so do men close their eyes to the light of truth. To such people philosophy is a kind of book, like the Aneid or the Odyssey, where the truth is to be sought, not in the universe or nature, but (I use their own words) by comparing texts!'

Galileo now used the immense fame he had acquired to achieve his ambition for a special position in Florence. He wrote to the Tuscan Secretary of State in May 1610, saying that he had devoted the twenty best years of his life to teaching, and 'dealing out (as one may say) in detail, and at the request of everybody', such knowledge as he could give. He now desired leisure to write three great works summarizing and expounding his discoveries. But he still had to teach and take pupils in order to support his relatives. He wanted to be freed from all these burdens, and return to his native land, and have the opportunity 'to gain my bread by my writings', which he would always dedicate to the Grand Duke, without having to perform any other duties.

He then outlined the works he proposed to write. There were to be two books on the system of the universe, 'an immense work, full of philosophy, astronomy, and geometry; three books on motion, 'a science entirely new'; three books on mechanics, and one each on sound and speech; on light and colours; on the tides; on the composition on continuous quantity; and on the movements of animals. He also had plans for some books on military science.

He had previously remarked that 'it is impossible to obtain from a Republic, however splendid and generous, a stipend without duties attached to it . . . In short, I have no hope of enjoying such ease and leisure as are necessary to me, except in the service of an absolute prince'.

The Grand Duke now offered him the position of First Mathematician of the University of Pisa, with a salary of 1000 scudi. It was a sinecure, for he was to be exempt from teaching duties, and from residence in Pisa. Galileo asked that the title of Philosopher and Mathematician to the Grand Duke should be added. This was agreed, and he was summoned to Florence in July, 1611.

His friends, and even he feared that he had made a mistake. The Venetian Republic had preserved its independence by playing their northern Protestant neighbours against the Vatican. Rome did not go to extremes against it, for fear that the Venetians would ally themselves with the northern countries, and thereby give the Reformation a foothold in Italy.

As part of their policy of strengthening the influence of Rome within the Republic, the Jesuits tried to capture the university of Padua by infiltration. The Venetian Senate countered this by banning them from delivering any kind of higher instruction in Padua. Then, in the middle of a night in May 1606, it physically expelled all Jesuits from the territory of the Republic.

Galileo made jokes about these events to his friends, and his attitude was not a happy augury for his future relations with the order.

His old friend Sagrado wrote to him in 1611 : 'where will you find the same liberty as in Venetian territory, and, notwithstanding all the good qualities of the young ruler of Tuscany, who can promise with any confidence that, if not ruined, you will not be persecuted and tossed on the surging billows of Court life by the raging storms of envy?'

But at first everything seemed to go on as brilliantly, and even more grandly than ever, under the absolute prince. A month after he had entered into his new post, he discovered the phases of Venus, which he regarded as a further confirmation of the Copernican theory, 'Kepler and the other Copernicans may now be proved to have judged and philosophized correctly . . .'

At this time, Galileo was at the height of his powers. He was about forty-six years old, of square build, and rather taller than the average. He had brilliant eyes, his hair was reddish, and he was naturally robust. His intellectual energy was prodigious, and he was physically energetic. In the second half of his life he suffered much from sleeplessness and rheumatism, perhaps exacerbated by his astronomical observations at night, without proper protection from the cold. He was incessantly active with his brain and hands, and was fond of saying that occupation is the best medicine for mind and body. He was irascible, and was impatient of what he thought to be nonsense.

When Galileo left Padua, he seems to have taken his two little girls with him, but left his mistress behind. He married her to a worthy man of the same station in life, Giovanni Bartoluzzi, and provided yet another handsome dowry. Bartoluzzi always behaved to Galileo with respectful cordiality.

In 1611 he decided to place both his daughters, one eleven years and the other ten, in a convent for life. He had to use much influence to secure dispensation from the very strict rule of admittance at the proper age. They were placed in the very poor but relatively well-run Franciscan convent of St. Matthew at Arcetri near Florence. They finally took the veil in 1616 and 1617, being then only sixteen years old. Galileo's incarceration of his daughters in conditions of poverty, when he himself had just accepted a very well-paid position, obviously raises serious questions. One of his better reasons may perhaps have been his own mother's difficult and bad temper. She may not have been disposed to be kind to his illegitimate children, and he did not feel that they would be properly looked after in his own house, without womanly care.

After his appointment at Florence, he made a grand visit to Rome, to demonstrate his 'celestial novelties'. A commission under Cardinal Bellarmine was appointed to investigate them. The heavens were observed through telescopes in the Cardinal's gardens, and a favourable report was issued. Galileo was granted a long audience with the Pope, Paul V, who assured him of his good will.

Immediately after the publication of the Bellarmine report, Galileo discovered the sun-spots, and deduced from them that the sun is rotating. He found himself involved in a dispute on priority with the Jesuit astronomer Scheiner, who claimed to have observed them earlier, but had not been allowed to publish his discovery because the local head of his order could find no reference to them in Aristotle. He was told that they were probably appearances due to the ' faults of your glasses, or your eyes '.

The sun-spot controversy was particularly unfortunate for Galileo, because it embroiled him with the Jesuits as an organization, determined to vindicate the discoveries of one of its members.

He returned to Florence, and made further important discoveries about the moon, and the mechanics of floating bodies.

Meanwhile, his enemies were not idle. They rallied their forces, and in the autumn of 1613, various monks in Florence leagued together to attack him and his ideas. They preached furious sermons against Copernicanism.

The Grand Duchess Christina, the mother of the duke, a very pious Frenchwoman under Church influence, took advantage of a ducal dinner-party to cross-examine Castelli, one of Galileo's best pupils, on the reality of the new planets. She repeated many arguments against it, and supported them with quotations from the Scriptures. Castelli reported the affair to Galileo, remarking that the Grand Duchess seemed to have been drawing him out.

Galileo immediately replied, giving his views on the relation between Scripture and science. He said that Scripture cannot err, but ' its interpreters and expounders are liable to err in many ways ', particularly by stopping ' short at the literal significance of the words '. According to the words, God was sometimes endowed with hands and feet, and emotions. The bare sense of many passages appeared contrary to the truth, owing to the necessity of accommodating expositions to the capacities of the vulgar. Scripture was capable of various interpretations, often different from the apparent meaning of the words, especially in matters involving mathematical principles. As both Scripture and nature emanated from the Divine word, ' those natural effects which the experience of the senses places before our eyes . . . are in no wise to be revoked because of certain passages in Scripture '.

He went on to say that ' Scripture has not abstained from veiling in shadow its principal dogmas, attributing to God himself conditions differing from, and contrary to, the Divine essence '. He implied that the Scriptural statements on astronomy may have been composed in a form to facilitate the salvation of the vulgar, rather than reveal scientific truth.

As it was impossible to be certain that all interpreters of Scripture were divinely inspired, it would be as well to forbid quotations from Scripture in support of ' what our senses, or demonstrated proof, may manifest to the contrary. Who can set bounds to the mind of man? Who dares assert that he already knows all that in this universe is knowable?'

Galileo then says: ' I believe that the intention of Holy Writ was to persuade men of the truths necessary to salvation; such as neither Science nor other means could render credible, but only the voice of the Holy Spirit. But I do not think it necessary to believe that the same God who gave us our senses, our speech, our intellect, would have us put aside the use of these, to teach us instead such things as with their help we could find out for ourselves, particularly in the case of these sciences, of which there is not the smallest mention in the Scripture, and, above all, in astronomy, of which so little notice is taken that the names of all the planets are not mentioned. Surely if the intention of the sacred writers had been to teach the people astronomy, they would not have passed the subject over so completely.'

When Galileo's wiser friends read this letter, their hair stood on end. It implied the fallibility of the Church, and the advocacy of the fundamental principle of Protestantism : personal interpretation of the Scriptures.

A copy of the letter soon found its way to Rome. The Inquisition requested the Archbishop of Pisa dextrously to secure the original. Galileo was advised to go to Rome to explain his opinions. He was overwhelmingly confident that any intelligent man must agree with him. He talked enthusiastically to his friends, and learned something of his opponents' activities, but not very much. He seemed unable to appreciate the magnitude and strength of the forces organized against him.

The Tuscan ambassador, Piero Guicciardini, reported to the Duke that he was much troubled by Galileo's behaviour. He had importuned many cardinals, and thrown himself on the favour of Cardinal Orsini (who was twenty-two years old). Orsini had argued with the Pope in Galileo's support, but had been cut short, and after he had gone, the Pope had discussed the matter with Bellarmine. They had decided that Galileo's opinions were erroneous and heretical, and Copernicus and other writers of the same opinions were to be corrected or prohibited.

He did not think that Galileo's person would suffer, as of course he would see the prudence of agreeing with what Holy Church willed. ' But he fires up in defence of his opinions, and he has small strength to control himself '. Consequently the climate of Rome was extremely dangerous to him, especially ' in these times, when we have a Pope who abhors *belles lettres* and geniuses '. Everyone sought to accommodate ' his own brain and nature to that of our lord Pope ', so that even those who knew something went about industriously pretending that they knew nothing. The ambassador could not see what good Galileo would do by remaining, and reminded the Grand Duke how much he owed to the Church of God, and to the Holy Inquisition. If his brother, Cardinal Carlo de Medici, came to Rome and supported the Copernican theory against the Inquisition, 'the very base and cornerstone of religion,' it would damage the standing of the family with the Church. It would be well if Galileo were recalled from Rome before the cardinal arrived, for 'Galileo is so vehement, so obstinate and so infatuated, that it is impossible for anyone who has him in his neighbourhood to escape his hands'.

Galileo was largely in the dark as to what was happening, for the Inquisition was proceeding with its usual secrecy. He wrote to the Duke that he had conducted himself with the utmost discretion. In spite of some misgivings, he believed he had been successful.

As he was preparing to return to Florence in triumph, the Inquisition issued without warning an examination of his work on sun-spots, and stated that his proposition that the sun was the centre of the world was 'false and absurd philosophically, and formally heretical', and the proposition that the earth is not the centre of the world, but moves, deserved the same censure.

Bellarmine was directed to admonish him not 'henceforth to hold, teach or defend' such doctrine. Galileo acquiesced, and 'promised to obey'. This record of the proceedings of the Inquisition was, of course, confidential, and remained secret for many years.

A few days later, on March 5th 1616, Copernicus' *Revolutions of the Celestial Spheres* was 'suspended until corrected'.

After Galileo had acquiesced, the Pope, Paul V, received him on March 11th, and walked up and down with him amiably for three quarters of an hour, assuring him that as long as he occupied the chair of St. Peter, he need not fear persecution.

Before he left Rome, Galileo obtained a declaration from Cardinal Bellarmine, certifying that he had not been submitted to any punishments, but had merely been informed of the Pope's declaration 'which adjudges the doctrine attributed to Copernicus, respecting the motion of the earth round the sun to be contrary to Scripture, and therefore not to be held nor defended'.

The last of these sentences had a vital part in Galileo's condemnation by the Inquisition seventeen years later, for it did not agree in a crucial point with the secret minute of the admonishment, which said that he should not hold, defend, nor *teach* the Copernican theory.

Galileo returned to Florence, humiliated and frustrated. He had long fits of depression, and found it difficult to work. His old Paduan friend Sagrado advised him to philosophize comfortably in his bed, and let the stars alone. Let fools be fools, let the ignorant plume themselves on their ignorance. Why should he court martyrdom for the sake of winning them from their folly? It was not given to everyone to be one of the elect, and for his part, he believed that the universe was made for him, and not he for the universe.

Not being able to work freely at home, Galileo used his energy in conducting a large correspondence with princes and philosophers. In 1618 he sent a treatise on the tides to the Archduke Leopold of Austria, and added in a long letter an explanation that his theory of this phenomenon is only 'a poetical conceit or a dream'. He had written it in haste, and 'in the expectation that the work of Copernicus would not be condemned as erroneous eighty years after its publication'. He had held the theory of Copernicus to be true, 'until it pleased those gentlemen to prohibit the work and declare that opinion to be false and contrary to Scripture '. But knowing as he did that ' it behoves us to obey the decisions of the authorities and to believe them, since they are guided by a higher insight than any to which my humble mind can of itself attain ', he could not offer his new theory of the tides to him as anything more than a fancy, for it was based on Copernican theory.

The year 1618 marked the opening of the Thirty Years' War, the desperate struggle between the Reformation and the Counter-Reformation, in which three-quarters of the whole population of Germany died. It happened that three prominent comets appeared in this year, which were commonly viewed as grave portents. There was great public concern over them. Both Galileo and the Jesuit astronomers produced new theories of comets to meet the current interest. Their theories were in conflict, and ultimately both proved to be wrong, but Galileo spent three years in writing a critique of the Jesuit theory, and expounding his own. This was in his pamphlet *The Assayer* (Il Saggiatore).

In this brilliant work, he not only expounded his theory of comets, but laid down the philosophy which has governed science for the last three centuries. He said in it that ' motion is the cause of heat ', and that he did ' not believe that there exists anything in external bodies for exciting tastes, smells, and sounds, but size, shape, quantity, and motion, swift or slow; and if ears, tongues, and noses were removed, I am of opinion that shape, quantity, and motion would remain, but there would be an end of smells, tastes, and sounds, which, abstractedly from the living creature, I take to be mere words '.

This is Galileo's separation of the primary qualities of bodies, their shape, etc., from their secondary qualities, their colour, etc. He supposed that physics was based on the primary qualities, and that the secondary qualities were subjective productions of the mind. It is the starting point of the philosophy not only of Newton, but also of Locke and Berkeley.

Then, in 1623, his old friend Cardinal Barberini was elected Pope, as Urban VIII. Barberini had enthusiastically followed Galileo's scientific researches for years, and even written verses in their honour. Galileo was once more inspired with great hopes that he would be able to persuade the Head of the Church to accept the Copernican doctrine.

Galileo dedicated *The Assayer* to Urban VIII, and was informed that he was delighted with it, and had it read to him at meal-times. It was the only book which was sufficiently interesting to distract his mind from the cares of his office.

The Jesuits were extremely angry with the book, and the situation. In 1625, *The Assayer* was denounced to the Inquisition, but received a favourable report.

Galileo had rented a villa on Bellosguardo Hill, outside Florence, in 1617. It was at about half an hour's walking distance from his daughters' convent. His children were growing up, and his eldest daughter, now called Sister Maria Celeste, proved to be a woman of charm, sense and fine character. His son Vincenzio, who had been legitimatized by the Grand Duke in 1619, turned out to be a wastrel, like his uncle Vincenzio, selfish, mulishly obstinate and 'as hard as a stone'.

Galileo came to depend more and more on Maria Celeste, whom he could call to see, but who could never leave her convent to come to see him. In 1631, he rented a little villa with a tower, within five minutes' walk of the convent at Arcetri, to be still nearer to Maria Celeste. After his condemnation, he was allowed to live there for the remainder of his life under house arrest. Galileo fortunately kept many of Maria Celeste's letters, but his to her were probably destroyed after she died in 1634, and he was 'vehemently suspected of heresy'.

Maria Celeste considered that she had no special claim on Galileo because she was born out of wedlock. She therefore regarded Galileo's kindness to her as magnanimous. The earliest of her letters which has survived was written in 1623 and is addressed to her 'very illustrious and most beloved lord and father'. But as the years went by, her father gradually acquired the true place in her filial imagination. She could not go to his house to look after him, but only imagine every detail from afar, even showing slight signs of jealousy, which she instantly recognized and suppressed, when he engaged a housekeeper.

The poor nuns were nearly always in ill-health. They often had not enough to eat, and Galileo's younger daughter seemed also to be slightly queer. The nuns had to change into summer underclothing in April, whether it was cold or not. Rheumatism was rife. Some of the nuns went mad. Maria Celeste recounted her terrible experiences with one who twice tried to commit suicide, the first time by banging her head on the stone floor until she was unrecognizable, and the second by cutting herself in fourteen places with a pen-knife. She died slowly, after being tied down in bed.

Maria Celeste showed no sign of mysticism. She believed in at least seven hours' sleep, and regretted she needed so much more than her father, who required so little. She was expert with her hands, an excellent cook, and the preparer of the convent's medicines. In this she was the true daughter of her father. She delighted to do little household tasks for him. Would he like some of her special baked pears or candied fruits (he was passionately fond of them) or would he prefer fragrant cinnamon water from the still-room? Do his collars require renewing, or mending? Would her father please send material to make some new ones for that unsatisfactory young brother? When she was herself ill and starving, she asked her father to send an old hen, too tough for anyone to eat, from which a little broth could be made.

Maria Celeste was overwhelmed with joy when she heard that her father's friend Barberini had become Pope. Seeing how many promises Barberini had made, perhaps it would be possible to 'get something for our brother'.

When she died in 1634, Galileo wrote that 'she was a woman of exquisite mind, singular goodness, and most tenderly attached to me'.

Galileo visited Rome in 1624, and tried to convert the new Pope to Copernicanism. He was very favourably received, and granted six long audiences, but Urban VIII would not accept it, nor would he raise the interdiction of 1616. He privately wrote 'that the Holy Church had not condemned the opinion of Copernicus nor was it condemned as heretical, but only as rash, and, moreover, if anyone could demonstrate it to be necessarily true, it would no longer be rash'.

Galileo returned home unsuccessful, but loaded with presents, and a pension for his son.

The Pope wrote to the Grand Duke that he observed in Galileo 'not only literary distinction, but love of religion' and had 'listened with pleasure to his learned demonstrations'.

Galileo decided to try to take advantage of the apparently friendly atmosphere to strike a more resounding blow for Copernicanism. He commenced to prepare the material for his great *Dialogues Concerning the Two Principal Systems of the World*. After six years' work, the manuscript was ready for the press. It was sent to Rome for permission to print. The Papal censor Riccardi, one of Galileo's old pupils, and favourable to him, saw that the Preface and Conclusion would be unacceptable. The Preface opens with the observation that 'there want not such as unadvisedly affirm that' the prohibition of Copernicanism 'was not the production of a sober scrutiny, but of an ill-informed Passion'. There had been mutterings that consultors 'altogether ignorant of astronomical observations ought not to clip the wings of speculative wits'. His zeal could not keep silence when he heard these 'inconsiderate complaints' and he determined, as a thoroughly informed person, to expound 'the naked truth'. It was obvious that Galileo's opening paragraphs were ironical.

The dialogues are conducted by three characters, Sagredo, Salviati and Simplicius. The latter is the spokesman of the old science and astronomy, and named after the great commentator on Greek mathematics. He comes in for much chaff, as the exponent of the Ptolemaic system and Aristotelian physics.

Galileo distilled forty years of research and meditation on astronomy into these dialogues, which expressed in final form his ideas and results, the chief of which have already been mentioned.

The last part was devoted to his theory of the tides. This was based on Copernicanism, and, indeed, it was evident that the heart of the work was with Copernicus. He was therefore advised, through Riccardi, to incorporate Urban VIII's own pet argument against Galileo's tidal theory, that 'God is omnipotent, all things are therefore possible to him. Therefore the tides cannot be adduced as a necessary proof of the double motion of the earth without limiting God's omnipotence'.

Galileo duly incorporated the argument, but in a garbled form, and he put it into the mouth of Simplicius, who had been the butt of the whole discourse. As Einstein has remarked, Galileo took an undiluted pleasure in personal controversy.

After reading this, Riccardi was still more nervous. Printing in Rome was delayed, so Galileo pressed that it should be done in Florence. Riccardi hesitated, and was only persuaded by Caterina Niccolini, the wife of the Grand Duke's gifted ambassador in Rome, to grant the permission.

Printing now proceeded, and the great work appeared in February 1632. Copies were immediately sent to personages in Rome. In August, the Holy Office ordered suspension of the sale of the book. The Grand Duke sent a letter of remonstrance, which had been drafted for him by Galileo, expressing surprise that the book should be suspended after the permission to print had been granted. Then Niccolini saw the Pope, and was surprised to find him very hostile. The Pope said that Galileo had deceived Riccardi in order to secure the permission to print, and he had not complied with the conditions that the Pope himself had laid down.

It was evident that the Pope was convinced that Galileo had secured the permission to print by sharp practice, and it seems probable that he was also convinced that Galileo had held him up to personal ridicule by putting his favourite argument into the mouth of Simplicius. Galileo and his friends believed that the change in the Pope's attitude was due especially to the influence of the Jesuits. Thenceforth the Pope pursued him with sharp personal rancour, his former exceptionally favourable attitude changing over into precisely its reverse.

He appointed a commission to report on the book, which proceeded in secret. All known to be favourable to Galileo were excluded from its membership. In a month's time, it reported that he had transgressed orders by asserting that the movement of the earth was real and not hypothetical, that he had been fraudulently silent on the command of 1616 that he should not ' hold, teach, or defend ' the Copernican theory, that he treated with contempt those who were opposed to the theory, that he had put the saving clause at the end of the *Dialogue* 'in the mouth of a simpleton', etc., etc.

Galileo was dumbfounded especially by the accusation of fraud with regard to the command of 1616, for in the certificate he had received at that time from Cardinal Bellarmine there was reference only to 'hold' and 'defend', but none to 'teach'. Evidently, if the Inquisition's minute of 1616 was correct, he was in a very serious position.

He was now summoned by the Inquisition to Rome for examination. He was not well, and he procrastinated, and finally he was told that if he did not come forthwith, he would be brought in chains. He arrived in reasonably good shape, and was treated with a consideration unique in the Inquisition's history, owing to the protection of the Grand Duke. He was allowed to stay in Ambassador Niccolini's house during the preliminary examination, and then was given comfortable rooms in the offices of the Inquisition, a concession never before made, even to princes. He was never put into the Inquisition's dungeons.

When he was examined, he pleaded ignorance of the prohibition to *teach,* as well as to hold and to defend Copernicanism, and he asserted that since 1616 he had never held or defended it.

After receiving the reports and hearing his evidence, the Inquisition tried him in his absence, as was its wont. Galileo was hopeful, but Niccolini, who handled his affairs with splendid skill, was amazed at his lack of political insight. He did not seem to understand the background of the affair at all. Galileo, who was always rating his opponents for attending more to words than to the realities of nature, seemed to think that he could defeat the Inquisition and extricate himself by verbal subtlety, as if political realities could be evaded by ingenious words. The Church was now in the midst of the Thirty Years' War, it dared not make concessions of any kind which served to impair its authority. With his thorough understanding of the political situation in Rome, Niccolini advised Galileo to be completely submissive. Galileo always insisted that he was a good Catholic, he was in the hands of the Inquisition, there was no other way.

Niccolini reported to the Grand Duke that he had advised Galileo that he must submit, and recommended him even to deny the earth's motion. 'This advice of mine' wrote Niccolini, 'has afflicted him extremely; so much so, that ever since yesterday he has been in such a state of prostration that I have fears for his life.'

Galileo had had occasion, in the past, to criticize the technical competence with which the fortifications of the Pope's Castle of St. Angelo had been carried out by the Commissary-General of the Inquisition, Firenzuola. He now found himself visited by the Commissary-General while imprisoned in the Inquisition's offices. After a long discussion with Firenzuola he made a confession, in which he said that he 'truly and sincerely held and do hold' his arguments for the motion of the earth from the tides, and from sun-spots to be 'inconclusive and admitting of refutation'. He had fallen into 'the natural complacency which every man feels with regard to his own subtlety', and he had devised ingenious and plausible arguments in favour of false propositions. 'My error, then, has been—and I confess it—one of vainglorious ambition, and of pure ignorance and inadvertence.'

Galileo also submitted a long statement in which he did not deny that in 1616 he had been admonished not to *teach* the Copernican theory, as well as not to hold or defend it, but 'I do not think I ought to be disbelieved when I urge that in the course of fourteen or sixteen years I had lost all recollection of them'.

He was allowed to return to Niccolini's house. He believed he would be released. But at a secret meeting presided over by Urban VIII, it was decided that Galileo was to be interrogated, 'and threatened with torture'.

He was summoned for examination a fourth time, and three times denied that he had held the Copernican opinion since 1616, and he affirmed that the Ptolemaic opinion was true. Finally, he was ordered to speak the truth, or he would be tortured. 'I am here to obey, and I have not held this opinion since the decision was pronounced, as I have stated.'

A few days later the Inquisition pronounced a long sentence in which he was 'vehemently suspected of heresy' on account of having believed and held that the sun was the centre of the world, etc. His *Dialogue* was prohibited, and he was to be imprisoned during the Holy Office's pleasure.

The aged and ailing philosopher was forced to kneel and recite a long recantation, in which he said that he 'must altogether abandon the false opinion that the sun is the centre of the world and immovable, and that the earth is not the centre of the world, and moves . . .' With 'sincere heart and unfeigned faith I adjure, curse, and detest the aforesaid errors and heresies'.

The story that as he rose from his knees he murmured: 'None the less, it moves!' seems to be quite unfounded, and it is extremely unlikely that after such an utter humiliation, he would have invited his immediate execution.

Galileo was permitted to stay at first with Niccolini, and then with the Archbishop of Siena. But after he had been there five months, the Inquisition's spies reported that he was again spreading heretical opinions. At the end of 1633 he was allowed to live, under surveillance, in his villa at Arcetri, near his daughters' convent.

Maria Celeste had been supervising his household from a distance; she was worn out by the strain and the hard life. To have a father under vehement suspicion of heresy and condemned by the Holy Office was a dreadful trial for a nun. But she never lost faith in her father. He was able to see her for the last time just before she died, early in 1634.

Alone, under strict surveillance, not allowed to receive general visitors, an old man of seventy with aching limbs and inflamed eyes, Galileo now prepared for the press his *Dialogues Concerning Two New Sciences*, the greatest of all his works, containing in particular the foundations of the new science of motion, and of the strength of materials. It is less spectacular than the *Dialogue on the Two Systems of the World*, but still more important.

He dedicated it to the Count de Noailles, the French Ambassador in Rome, and smuggled the manuscript out of Italy, to be published by Elzevir at Leiden in Holland. He wrote a dedication in which he pretended that the book had been printed against his will. The manuscript was ready for the press in 1636.

Even now, at the age of seventy-three, he was still making discoveries. In 1637 he noticed the phenomenon of the moon's libration, that its face is not always quite the same, but around its edges there are parts that are sometimes visible, and sometimes in shade. Newton afterwards showed that it is due to slight irregularities in the moon's revolution round the earth.

Later in the year, he lost the sight of his left eye, and in 1638 became totally blind. 'Alas,' he wrote, ' your dear friend and servant Galileo has been for the last month hopelessly blind; so that this heaven, this earth, this universe, which I by marvellous discoveries and clear demonstrations had enlarged a hundred thousand times beyond the belief of the wise men of bygone ages, henceforward for me is shrunk into such small space as is filled by my own bodily sensations.'

After he had become blind his surveillance was relaxed, and he had many visitors. Among these was Milton, who reported that 'there it was that I found and visited the famous Galileo, grown old, a prisoner to the Inquisition for thinking in Astronomy otherwise than the Franciscan and Dominican licencers thought'. In his defence of freedom of thought, he recounted how in Italy ' where this kind of inquisition tyrannizes, when I have sat among their learned men (for that honour I had) and been counted happy to be born in such a place of philosophic freedom as they supposed England was, while themselves did nothing but bemoan the servile condition into which learning amongst them was brought—that this was it which had damped the glory of Italian wits, that nothing had been there written now these many years but flattery and fustian '.

Besides many visitors, Galileo also at the last had talented assistance. Torricelli became his amanuensis. Almost at the very end, he described a design for a pendulum clock, which his son drew according to his instructions.

His health finally declined in 1641, and on January 8th, 1642, he died. The Inquisition refused the Court and citizens of Florence to give him a public funeral, and to erect a marble mausoleum for his grave. Permission for the latter was not obtained until 1737.

The spiritual truths to be learned today from Galileo's struggle, how to emulate his courage and avoid his mistakes, are at least as important as the natural truths that were learned from his marvellous physical discoveries. Thus mankind is trebly indebted to him for showing it how to make discoveries in the realm of nature, how to expound and fight for the truth, and also for serving as a warning of errors to be avoided in dealing with scientific results which have a moral and social significance.

REFERENCES

Galileo: His Life and Work, by J. J. Fahie. John Murray: 1903.

The Private Life of Galileo, by Mrs Allan-Olney. Macmillan: 1870.

Galileo and the Freedom of Thought, by F. Sherwood Taylor. Watts: 1938.

ISAAC NEWTON
1642 - 1727

THE Polish ecclesiastic Copernicus first looked at the world
in the modern way. The Italian master of profane knowledge, Galileo, showed how to investigate it. Armed with
the new point of view and method, Isaac Newton at one
blow gave a comprehensive account of the whole physical
universe as then known. No single intellectual feat in all
history has approached this in brilliance. He got more results, of greater importance, and in a shorter time, than any
other scientist.

How and why was it reserved to an English grammar
school boy and Trinity don to excel all the scientific geniuses
of ancient and modern times? There was evidently something very special in both his intellect and his circumstances.

Isaac Newton was born on Christmas Day, 1642, at
Woolsthorpe, a little country hamlet about seven miles
from Grantham, in Lincolnshire. His father was lord of the
manor, but this was only a tiny estate, consisting of a manor
house and farm and a few cottages. The rent from the whole
estate was about £30 a year. Newton senior was in fact a
yeoman farmer, with the title of a gentleman. He died a
few months after he was married, and before his son was
born. He had the reputation of being 'a wild, extravagant
and weak man'. Very little is known of his ancestry.

His wife Hannah came from Rutland. She was a pious,
good and capable woman. Besides losing her husband before
her son was born, she almost lost her son too, for he was

premature. He was so small, she used to say, that he could have been put into a quart pot. After he was born, the two midwives set out to get some things from a neighbour, not expecting that he would be alive on their return. But the infant survived, and a profound attachment grew between the mother and her child.

Hannah Newton managed the farm and reared her son for two years, and was then informed that the Reverend Barnabas Smith, a bachelor clergyman of mature years, was looking for a capable wife. Mr. Smith had a substantial private income of £500 a year, in addition to his living. As he was a very shy man, one of his parishioners proposed to Mrs. Newton on his behalf. She accepted him on the conditions that he repaired the manor house, agreed that Isaac should retain the income from the manor, and that he should settle an additional estate of £50 a year on the boy.

The Newtons regarded themselves as mildly royalist, as became titular gentlemen-farmers, but it is evident that the widow Newton combined piety and business in the typical puritan manner. She brought forth her son at the beginning of the Civil War, near the region from which Cromwell drew his Ironsides.

All of these circumstances had a profound influence on Isaac Newton's life and achievements. He grew up in a district permeated with puritan ideas, during the Civil War, but with the title of a lord of the manor. Newton was deeply concerned throughout his life with individual protestant thinking and the sustained desire to establish himself as a gentleman.

How different was his position from that of Copernicus, reared within the bosom of the Catholic Church, and Galileo imprisoned by its tyranny. When Newton appeared, a clean sweep had already been made of Catholic influence and tyranny from his environment. Nor was Newton ever poor. His income was never less than £80 a year.

His mother went to live with her second husband, and left him at the age of two with his grandmother at the manor house. He grew into a gentle docile child who preferred making things to playing with other boys. He shrank from hunting and any kind of physical cruelty. In rough company, he was inclined to be silent and withdraw into himself, and the habit of secrecy grew on him. It has been suggested that these inhibitions, which became such a feature of his later behaviour, may have had something to do with his extreme frailty at birth. He had an inner constitutional delicacy that he never grew out of, though he externally became a hale and courageous man, and lived to a great age.

He attended village schools as a child, and showed no special aptitudes. The only notable activity of his childhood was model-making, which is common among boys, but in his case better authenticated than usual.

When he was twelve, he was sent to the King's School at Grantham. This had been founded in 1528, during the reign of Henry VIII. As it was seven miles away, he was placed in lodgings, like many farmers' sons today who are sent from the country to attend the grammar school in the local market town. He stayed with the apothecary Mr. Clark, whose wife was a close friend of Isaac's mother.

The excellent Mr. Clark allowed and encouraged him to spend school holidays 'entirely in knocking and hammering in his lodging room', with little saws, hatchets, hammers and all sorts of tools. He made a model of a new windmill that had recently been built at Grantham. He put the model on the roof of the house to catch the wind. And in it was a mouse, 'which he called the miller'. The mechanism was so arranged that the mouse could set the mill going at any moment, and Isaac 'would joke too upon the miller eating the corn that was put in'. He made a waterclock four feet high, and in later life spoke to Halley on the difficulties caused by the furring-up through impurities of the fine hole through which the water escapes. He made kites, which he flew at night, with lamps tied to their tails, 'which at first affrighted the country people exceedingly, thinking they were comets'.

Isaac not only found a most sympathetic home from home with Mr. Clark, but also the closest friend of his youth. This was Mr. Clark's little step-daughter, Miss Storey. When Newton left Woolsthorpe to go to Cambridge he was engaged to her, but their emotional attachment gradually faded into mutual esteem and life-long friendship. Miss Storey afterwards recalled that Isaac 'was always a sober, silent, thinking lad, and was never known scarce to play with the boys abroad, at their silly amusements; but would rather choose to be at home, even among the girls, and would frequently make little tables, cupboards, and other utensils for her and her playfellows, to set their babies and trinkets on'.

Newton never forgot Miss Storey. In her old age he saw her during his visits to his home, and he continually gave her presents, including sums of forty shillings (quite a useful amount in those days) whenever she needed them.

Mr. Clark had a large number of chemicals and bottles which instantly fascinated the boy, and in his attic Isaac found a parcel of interesting scientific books. Newton retained ever afterwards a passionate interest in alchemy. He spent more time and effort on trying to transmute metals into gold, and find the elixir of life, than he devoted to his prodigious works in mathematics, astronomy and physics.

At the King's School, among the other sons of farmers and local professional people, he continued to learn Scripture and arithmetic, and began Latin, ancient history and elementary geometry. He made no impression as a scholar, until he was kicked in the stomach by another boy. This provoked a fight, in which Isaac, egged on by the head-master's son, had the better of it. He was urged to rub the other boy's nose on the wall, and in the end succeeded. After this, he began to exert himself, and gradually worked his way to the top of the class, and finally of the school, but he never appeared to be very exceptional, or any better than the ordinary clever school-boy. He was not precocious.

After he had been attending the school for four years, his mother withdrew him, at the age of sixteen. Her second husband had died, leaving her a well-to-do woman with a second family of three children, another son and two daughters. She moved back to Woolsthorpe with her young family, and needed Isaac to help with the management of the farm. He failed completely in this. When he was sent into Grantham on market days with one of the old farm hands, he used to disappear as quickly as possible into Mr. Clark's attic and bury himself in the chemical books. On the farm he used to retire under a hedge and read a book, or carve models with his knife, instead of looking after the animals.

At home, he fitted up a room with shelves for his books, and a work table for his tools. He drew pictures, which he hung on the walls, in frames that he had made himself. One of his chief occupations was making sun-dials. Several of these are still to be seen on the walls of the manor house at Woolsthorpe.

He spent a good deal of time in making drawings and calculations, but these were probably quite subsidiary to the design of his models. There is no evidence that he was specially interested in pure science and mathematics in his boyhood.

It was evident that Isaac was not cut out to be a farmer, so Mrs. Newton consulted her relations and friends on his future. Mr. Stokes, his old headmaster, urged that he should return to the King's School and be prepared for entrance to the university. Mrs. Newton's brother, the Reverend William Ayscough, rector of Burton Coggles, counselled that he should go to his own college, Trinity College, Cambridge.

After being away from school for a year, Isaac returned to be prepared for Cambridge. He was coached in Biblical criticism, Latin, classical history, Greek, logic, and the earlier propositions in Euclid. It was presumed that he would graduate at Cambridge, and prepare to take holy orders. He was taught mathematics by Dr. Clark M.D., who had been a pupil of Henry More at Cambridge, and was the brother of Mr. Clark, to whose house, and the company of Miss Storey, he now returned.

Isaac was well on the way to adding his name to the list of eminent old boys at the King's School, at the head of which was William Cecil, Lord Burghley, perhaps the greatest of English statesmen. Another was Henry More, who had recently preceded him to Cambridge, and became the leader of the Cambridge Platonists. Newton later was very friendly with More, and was much influenced by him in his formulation of his ideas of space and time.

Newton was not isolated, except by his own self-contained nature, and the ivory tower which he built for himself. Throughout his life he was in comfortable circumstances and sympathetic society, and from his boyhood was in contact with many of the greatest traditions.

Newton began to keep notebooks when he was a boy. Two of these have survived, and the earlier of them, after being lost for more than a century, was found in the Pierpont Morgan Library in New York. Newton started his notebooks from one end, and then, some years later, turned them and used them from the other. Judging from the immaturity of the handwriting, he began this notebook during the ages of thirteen to sixteen. It opens with ten pages of notes on drawing and painting, copied from a book by John Bate. He was evidently very much interested in drawing and painting, and it is said that he covered the walls of his room with drawings of 'birds, beasts, men, ships, and mathematical schemes'. Then there are several pages dealing with medicines, purges for the head, and 'an excellent plaster of his for corns'.

After this, under the heading 'Certain tricks' are various conjuring devices, one of which is 'to turn water into wine'. He made notes on general knowledge, in the period when he was supposed to be helping with the farm, on 'arts, trades and sciences', 'Householdstuff', 'meat and drink', minerals, husbandry, and 'of man, his affections and senses'.

Another section, which may have been written when he was an undergraduate, contains a scheme for reformed spelling on the phonetic principle, and shows a knowledge of the letters of the Hebrew alphabet.

Newton went up to Trinity College, Cambridge, in June 1661, shortly after the Restoration of Charles II in 1660. He was thus a post-war student, subject to all the stimulation and disorganization that occurs in these periods. The universities had been centres of the struggle between Puritans and Royalists, who, according to their ascendancy, changed the heads of colleagues and other officers. Cromwell himself had established his military headquarters in Emanuel College.

When Newton arrived, the university had lost many of its leading scholars, and the post-Restoration students, from the recent tension, were wild and disorderly. The undergraduates shared rooms in pairs, and one of the earliest records of Newton at Cambridge is of his wandering distraught round the Great Court of Trinity, in the middle of the night, to escape from a riotous party given by the man with whom he shared rooms. He ran into another student in a similar case, so the two quiet men decided to exchange companions, and room together.

Newton entered the college in the humblest academic status as a sub-sizar, or servant to his tutor, for whom he brought food from the college kitchen, and ran errands. In return for this, he received free tuition and board. Newton was probably very conscious of not being a great gentleman's son, and at the same time, as lord of the little manor of Woolsthorpe, he regarded himself as above the rank of artizans. He was not without connections in Trinity. The Senior Fellow, Dr. H. Babington, an important man in the history of the college, was related to Mr. Clark, the apothecary.

Newton's first undergraduate years were undistinguished. He probably went over his grammar-school studies in Latin and mathematics more thoroughly, and learned some Greek. With his introverted nature he no doubt did not mix very intimately with the other post-Restoration students, but appeared a quiet nondescript harmless young man admirably fitted to become an obscure country rector.

His little notebook records the kind of expenses he incurred when he first went up to Trinity. It shows that in many things he was much like other men. For instance, he spent on:

	£	s.	d.
Stilton		2	0
Cambridge White Lion		2	6
A chamber pot		2	2
A table to set down the number of my clothes in the wash		1	0
A paper book			8
For a quart bottle and ink to fill it . .		1	7

The most ambitious of these purchases seems to have been the quart of ink, which could certainly have gone a long way.

Then one more big link in his long chain of good fortune fell into place: the great Isaac Barrow transferred from the regius professorship of Greek to the new chair of mathematics founded by Lucas in 1663. Barrow was a fellow of Trinity and a royalist, who had gone into exile in 1655, and engaged in battles with pirates in Eastern Europe. He was a distinguished Greek scholar, and a mathematician and physicist of European status, who, like Pascal and Wallis, almost discovered the calculus before Newton, and a still more eminent divine. He was a small man of immense physical strength and vivacious personality, and a great favourite of Charles II, who thoroughly enjoyed listening to his excoriating sermons on His Majesty's frivolities.

Barrow became Newton's tutor in 1663, and it is from about that time that Newton's genius unfolded with startling power. This remarkable man, who could admonish kings, seems to have been a sufficiently great man himself to unlock Newton's hitherto closed genius.

Barrow examined Newton for a scholarship at Trinity in 1664. Newton was already twenty-two, and was merely one among forty-five successful candidates. It is said that Barrow reported that his knowledge of Euclid was unsatisfactory. It seems that Newton had found the propositions obvious, and had not stopped to consider the logical development of the subject as an example of rigorous method. In later years he used to say that he regretted having mastered Descartes' algebraical geometry before he had 'considered the elements of Euclid with that attention' which they deserved.

Newton advanced so far that Barrow took the opportunity of resigning the Lucasian chair of mathematics in his pupil's favour, in order to devote the whole of his time to his favourite passion for divinity. Barrow not only fired Newton's genius but handed to him at the age of twenty-six his own university chair. Newton was incomparable but he enjoyed a most encouraging environment.

The first notebook of Newton contains his earliest known notes on the Copernican theory, probably made in 1661. Newton himself stated that he read the works of Descartes, Wallis and other mathematicians in 1663. He studied Barrow's writings on optics. These appealed to him particularly, and led him to his first major published scientific work.

The winning of the Trinity scholarship in 1664 was a very important event in Newton's career. It launched him definitely on the academic life and gave him the opportunity for several years' uninterrupted study.

Trinity College had been founded in 1546 by Henry VIII, and endowed with rich spoils from the dissolution of the monasteries. Indeed, Henry VIII, as one of the great instruments of the Reformation, had an immense influence on modern science, by creating the conditions in which it could develop. It was he who was excommunicated by Paul III, the patron of Copernicus and refounder of the Inquisition. By removing England from the domination of the Catholic Church he created the conditions in which her scientists could work, free from the patronage, and the persecution of the Vatican.

Not only that, one of his father's ministers was the founder of Newton's school at Grantham, and he himself was the founder and endower of the college which provided Newton with such excellent educational training and material support.

Through the person of Henry VIII, the Reformation had swept from the path that lay before Newton both the religious and material obstacles which had confronted Copernicus and Galileo. Newton's genius was unexampled, but the path for him had already been cleared. The combination of these two circumstances produced results of such startling magnitude that they seemed almost super-human.

As a scholar, Newton's abilities were now thoroughly aroused. He had been taught geometry and optics by a master, and he had learned Descartes' algebraical geometry. The effect of Descartes' great invention, which arose out of Galileo's work, was to use the facilities of algebra for calculating the arrangement of points and lines in space. It reduced geometry to a system which anyone with moderate abilities could use, and greatly reduced dependence on exceptional intuition for making discoveries.

Newton puzzled out Descartes' book (made intentionally difficult by Descartes in order to evade popularity, and hence, persecution) for himself. Though he had unequalled mathematical ability, he did not care much for mathematics as such. He regarded it as a tool in the exploration of nature, and a means for the precise expression of scientific laws. His personal bias was for experiments. Apart from a brief period in his early days, he did not cultivate mathematics for its own sake.

Before he graduated in January 1665, he devoted a great deal of effort to optics, following Barrow, and making experiments on the refraction of light, and the grinding of lenses. He read Kepler's *Optics*, which aroused his interest in telescopes.

His interest in mathematics was subordinate to his interest in the workings of the real material world. No doubt this was one of the reasons why his mathematical powers lay dormant, and were not exhibited until after he had discovered features of the material world to which they could be applied effectively. Newton was essentially a child of the protestant practical life.

After his graduation, his expense books show a modest relaxation :

	£	s.	d.
Drills, grovers, a hone, a hammer, and a mandril		5	0
A magnet		16	0
Compasses		3	6
Glass bubbles		4	0
At the tavern several times	1	0	0

In those days a very considerable number of drinks could be bought for one pound. In the next year or two, we hear of :

	£	s.	d.
The Hist. of the Royal Society		7	0
Lost at cards twice		15	0
To three prisms		3	0	0
Four ounces of putty		1	4
Bacon's Miscellanies		1	6
For oranges for my sister		4	2
For aquafortis, sublimate, oyle pink, fine silver, antimony, vinegar, spirit of wine, white lead, salt of tartar	2	0	0
Lent Wardwell 3s., and his wife 2s.		5	0

These notes reveal Newton as a normal young man, with a strong interest in physical and chemical experiments, and kindly relations with relatives and friends. They also show that he was able to buy anything he wanted, within reason.

Newton had now acquired a thorough command of contemporary mathematics, and his mind was seething with interest in physical things. He might have been overcome by mental indigestion, or been diverted into academic teaching and affairs. But he was saved by the arrival of the Great Plague. The bubonic plague had infected London in 1664, and appeared in Cambridge in the following year. The university was closed, and its members dispersed into the country. Newton went home to Woolsthorpe at the beginning of August 1665, and remained there until the end of March 1666. He was able to submit the contents of his mind to eight months of undisturbed meditation. In a period of two years he spent more time at Woolsthorpe than at Cambridge, and in this period, he made three of the greatest scientific discoveries.

Galileo had shown how to investigate the motion of a body by resolving it into two motions along lines at right angles to each other. Descartes showed how to use algebra to simplify calculations about the geometry of Galileo's figures. Descartes found that points and lines could be represented by an algebraical equation. But his method provided only snapshots, at any particular moment, as it were, of a point in motion. The next step was the invention of a mathematical method which would enable Descartes' algebraical geometry to be applied, not only to points and lines at rest, but to points and lines in motion, and hence to the analysis of the motion of actual bodies in space.

Barrow, Pascal, Wallis and other great mathematicians were on the brink of this discovery, but it was first achieved by Newton. Early in 1665 he described a general method of making calculations about continuous changes in curves and areas. He later called it the method of fluxions, and it is now known as the differential and integral calculus. With it, he worked out the area of the hyperbola for the first time, and, glorying in his triumph, carried out the computation to fifty-two places of decimals. He did this in November, 1665, at Woolsthorpe.

He also discovered the binomial theorem, and the general method of expression of algebraical functions in infinite series, which was almost as great a contribution to pure mathematics as the calculus itself.

Optics were even more to his taste. He ground lenses with passionate energy, even making some of non-spherical shape. In attempts to make telescopes through which things could be seen without being fringed with colours, he was led to investigate the way in which light is refracted by prisms. He discovered that white light can be resolved into bundles of individual coloured rays, and that a prism bent the rays in increasing amount, from the red to the violet.

He concluded that owing to the different degrees in which the various coloured rays are refracted by a lens, the construction of a refracting telescope free from coloured fringes, or chromatic aberrations, was impossible. It was subsequently discovered that chromatic aberration can be reduced to a degree which is negligible in practice.

Newton, however, abandoned the telescope with lenses, and went over to the reflecting telescope, which magnifies by reflection from a mirror, which is free from chromatic aberration. Such a telescope was first proposed by James Gregory, but he did not make one. Newton was thus the first to make a reflecting telescope. It was six inches long, with a metallic mirror about one inch in diameter, and the whole mounted on a sphere, so that it could be pointed in any direction. As Newton subsequently remarked, it would 'discover as much as any three or four foot tube', and he forecast that in the future reflectors six feet long would be made, which would 'perform as much as any sixty or hundred foot tube made after the common way', that is, with lenses.

Newton presented a copy of this famous instrument, the prototype of all its successors, including the 200-inch giant at Mount Palomar, to the Royal Society. It was the first of his great achievements to be published, and was the particular piece of work for which the Royal Society elected him a fellow, in 1672.

Newton did not make astronomical observations, as he was short-sighted.

His discovery that white light can be resolved into individual coloured rays, which cannot be further resolved, was of profound importance, for an individual ray is capable of precise mathematical description. It made the properties of light susceptible to mathematical analysis.

The material universe consists of radiation and matter. Light is one of the forms of radiation, and the laws which govern it are the same as those which govern other forms, such as heat rays and radio rays. Thus, when Newton discovered how to treat light mathematically, he brought, as it were, one half of the universe under the reign of mathematical law.

He now proceeded to deal with the other half, the matter in the universe. Newton had learned Copernicus' conception of the universe, and Kepler's laws which describe the motion of the planets around the sun in ellipses. He had mastered Galileo's laws of motion, and the mechanics of moving bodies. He was familiar with Descartes' imaginative extension of Galileo's ideas to the whole universe, in which this was conceived as an articulating mechanical system. But Descartes' conception was merely a bold speculation. He could only offer faulty guesses as to how the universal machine actually worked.

During the plague years, Newton sat in his garden at Woolsthorpe, meditating on the great ideas of his predecessors, and trying to think of how the revolving planets and stars were actually kept going. It was natural for him to wonder whether the planets moved according to the same laws as those which Galileo had found to govern the motion of bodies falling to the earth. No doubt his casual observation of an apple falling from a tree was one of many factors which suggested that the laws which governed motion on the earth also applied to the motion of the planets. The force which pulled the apple to the earth was of the same kind as that which pulled the moon toward the earth, and the earth toward the sun.

Writing of this time, Newton himself said that he began to think of gravity extending to the moon. From a consideration of Kepler's law of the time of revolution of a planet, he deduced that the force which keeps the planet in its orbit must be inversely proportional to the square of its distance from the centre about which it revolves. Then he compared the force requisite to keep the moon in her orbit with the force of gravity as found at the surface of the earth, 'and found them answer pretty nearly'.

So Newton had discovered, before the end of 1666, that the motions of the planets could be explained in general terms by the law of gravitation. He had found the key to the description of the other half of the universe, that part of it consisting of matter in motion. He kept this general idea a profound secret, for immense mathematical researches were needed to prove it in detail.

He had made three tremendous discoveries, and he referred to the achievement in his own sublime words: 'All this was in the two plague years of 1665 and 1666, for in those days I was in the prime of my age for invention, and minded mathematics and philosophy more than at any time since'.

Newton put all these discoveries, together with several others almost as great, in his drawer, and did not begin to publish even a part of them until several years later. Discussion with others had no part in his processes of discovery.

His imagination was now profoundly absorbed in his mechanical description of the universe, and no doubt at this time his idea of marriage to Miss Storey passed away. If he had married, he would have forfeited the prospect of a fellowship at Trinity, and hence of the conditions for the undisturbed pursuit of scientific study. Miss Storey indicated in her old age that 'her portion being not considerable', she would not have been able to compensate Newton for losing a fellowship if she had married him, and she thought that 'perhaps his studies too' precluded it. Among many other things, Newton had had a very generous-spirited fiancée. But he, like his mother, had his emotions under business-like control.

Though Newton had discovered a general mechanical description of the universe, he was in no hurry to work out the details. He showed no desire whatever to draw attention to his achievement, and secure the esteem that it merited, though later he exhibited an intensely jealous resentment of any querying of his priorities.

He returned to Cambridge, after the plague had subsided, in 1667, and later in that year was elected a fellow of Trinity College. Two of the vacancies were due to fellows falling down stairs, and one to insanity.

In 1669, Barow sent a paper by Newton on his fluxions to John Collins, describing the author as a young man 'who, with an unparalleled genious, has made very great progress in this branch of mathematics'. He was happy to vacate his chair for Newton in the same year.

The salary of the Lucasian professor was about £100 a year, so now Newton had a comfortable income of at least £200 a year, in addition to board and lodging. His professorial duties were very light. He had to give only twenty-four lectures a year, and hold twice as many conferences with students. Often no one came to his lectures. He used to wait around the lecture room for a few minutes, and if no one came, return to his study. He had very few auditors, for his material was even more novel than relativistic quantum mechanics is today. He was no teacher with a mission to communicate his ideas to others.

Shortly after his appointment to the professorship, he wrote to Collins: 'I see not what there is desirable in public esteem, were I able to acquire and maintain it. It would perhaps increase my acquaintance, the thing which I chiefly study to decline'.

He settled down to a quiet college life, devoting a great deal of his time to alchemy and theology. By 1679 he had moved into rooms on the first floor, between the Great Gate and the Chapel in Trinity College. There was a wooden staircase which enabled him to walk down to a little square garden bounded by Trinity Street. He had a shed fitted up with furnaces and apparatus for alchemical experiments.

In appearance he was rather short, and in his youth, slight. His jaw was square, and his features rather sharp. His brow was broad, and his eyes, which protruded, were brown. His luxurious hair turned white before he was thirty. He had a very long nose. His early portraits show great force of expression, with a fierce mouth. Later ones reveal an apprehensive suspicious look. The latest represent him as a pink, portly, amiable old gentleman.

Bishop Atterbury said that 'In the whole of his face and make, there was nothing of that penetrating sagacity which appears in his compositions; he had something rather languid in his look and manner, which did not raise any great expectation in those who did not know him'. He spoke little in company, 'so that his conversation was not agreeable'.

On the other hand, his niece's husband, Conduitt, said that he 'had a lively and piercing eye'. Henry More wrote in 1680 that he had lent his *Exposition of the Apocalypse* to Newton, who came to his rooms, and spoke of it enthusiastically. More described how 'the manner of his countenance which is ordinarily melancholy and thoughtful' became 'mightily lightsome and cheerful' by 'the free profession of what satisfaction he took therein'.

Evidently, Newton was already passionately interested in the interpretation of prophecies, and his eyes and personality were illuminated when his emotional beliefs were touched.

As a son of a puritan region, Newton grew up with a strong interest in theology. In his life, he devoted at least as much effort to it as to science. He seems to have concluded at an early age that the doctrine of the Holy Trinity was an error, based on spurious passages smuggled into the Scriptures by Athanasius. He was probably an Arian heretic, or what is now called a unitarian.

His tendency to withdraw from life and conceal discoveries seems to have been strengthened by his desire to bury his horrible heretical secret. It prevented him from taking holy orders, and his lack of ordination subsequently made it impossible for him to become the Master of Trinity College. His heresy was peculiarly embarrassing to a Trinity man, for his college was dedicated by its founder Henry VIII to 'the Holy and Undivided Trinity'.

Newton left a vast mass of theological writings, which were deposited in a strong wooden chest by his heirs. During the later eighteenth century, one or two bishops opened the lid, glanced at the papers, but without proceeding very far, hastily slammed the lid down again, and said nothing.

In his discussion on the notion of the Holy Trinity, he gave fourteen arguments, supported by passages from the Scriptures, to show that the Son is neither coeternal with, nor equal to, the Father. He wrote that '*Homoousion* is unintelligible. 'Twas not understood in the Council of Nice . . . nor ever since. What cannot be understood is no object of belief'. This remained unpublished until 1934.

In his book on Daniel and the Apocalypse of St. John, he writes that 'The authority of Emperors, kings and princes, is human. The authority of councils, synods, bishops and presbyteries, is human. The authority of the prophets is divine, and comprehends the sum of religion, reckoning Moses and the Apostles among the prophets; and if an angel from heaven preach any other gospel, than what they have delivered, let him be accursed'. He considered that the rejection of the prophecies of Daniel was the rejection of the Christian religion, 'for this religion is founded upon his prophecy concerning the Messiah'. This language shows that Newton and Milton were akin in their source of inspiration.

But what about that rather languid look and manner? In his old age, he became the greatest ornament of the dullest of all courts: Queen Anne's. It seems that he was a quiescent intellectual volcano, slumbering peacefully in Her Majesty's drawing room, in the highest odour of respectability, while all the time, heresy smouldered underneath.

His first course of lectures as a professor in 1669 was on optics, and news of their remarkable contents reached the Royal Society. He was invited to send communications to them, and he began by sending a copy of his reflecting telescope, which is still one of the Society's most valued possessions. It excited great interest, and was examined by Charles II, Christopher Wren, Hooke, and many others. Newton wrote to the Society that he 'was surprized to see so much care taken about securing an invention to me, of which I have hitherto had so little value', and he gave thanks for his election as a fellow.

He was pressed for more information, and gave very full practical details of how the telescope was made. He introduced improvements in craftsmen's technique, such as the use of pitch in grinding lenses, which are still employed in the optical industry. He performed a great deal of physical labour in grinding his lenses, and had the strength and stamina of an experienced craftsman. No doubt he owed his strong constitution to the healthy life on the family farm in his youth. He could hold his own with any workman.

The perfection of his optical experiments shows that he must have devoted a great deal of time to them, for fundamental experiments are perfected only after innumerable preliminary trials. In addition to all this, he found time and energy for unequalled theoretical investigations.

In spite of his disparaging remarks on the telescope, Newton was gratified by its reception, and now offered to send the Society a paper which he did not doubt they would find more interesting, for it would contain in his 'judgment the oddest, if not the most considerable detection, which hath hitherto been made in the operations of nature'.

These were bold words from a young professor who had previously not published anything, but they were justified. In 1671 he sent a wonderful paper to the Royal Society, containing his capital discovery of the spectrum, and the resolution of white light into its component coloured rays. Even more remarkable than the facts themselves was his exhibition of how the scientific method should be applied in order to derive a new theory from the newly-discovered facts.

Incidentally, in discussing how the rays of light came to be bent by the prism he remarked how he 'had often seen a tennis ball, struck with an oblique racket, describe such a curveline. For, a circular as well as a progressive motion being communicated to it by that stroke, its parts on that side, where the motions conspire, must press and beat the contiguous air more violently than on the other, and there excite a reluctancy and reaction of the air proportionately greater . . .'

It seems that he was familiar with tennis courts, and may perhaps have played tennis. Thus the explanation of the swerve, exploited by such masters as W. T. Tilden and A. V. Bedser in tennis and cricket, was explained by Isaac Newton in his first published paper. That swerving ball haunted Newton's imagination all his life, and led him to his suggestion that light consists of particles subject to fits of easy bending, imposed on them by a system of waves. In 1924, Louis de Broglie proposed the modern wave-theory of matter, in which particles are supposed to be guided by waves of probability, in a somewhat similar way.

This first paper of Newton contained the first exhibition of the modern scientific method in its full maturity. It has remained the pattern of research method ever since. Experiment and theory are combined with a ruthless economy, in which every point is fundamental, and all extraneous considerations have been pruned away. It is written in Newton's leonine style, and it at once made a profound impression.

So far, Newton had appeared a reasonably normal man, shy and retiring, but in that not different from thousands of scholars before and since. He had been reserved about publishing his work, but he had been prepared to supply some accounts of it to qualified persons and societies, and he had been pleased with the appreciation it received. But his wonderful first paper on light at once lifted him from obscurity into the front rank of international science.

Other very gifted men had been at work in the same field, especially Robert Hooke, who was professional experimenter to the Royal Society. He had published in 1665 a great book called *Micrographia*, in which he described many new optical observations. No one has had more experimental fertility than Hooke. But he had not Newton's command of scientific method in using his experiments to decide questions of principle, nor his command of mathematics, by which theories describing them could be expressed in equations, from which new implications could be deduced. Hooke had experimented on almost every thing which was possible in his day, and had had many flashes of theoretical insight into their explanation, which he could not completely substantiate. Thus, when any new work was published, he always felt he had been there before. He acquired the habit of claiming the priority of other people's discoveries, for it was frequently true that he had already had the new ideas in a half-formulated and inconclusively proved form. He was a sickly, querulous man, who had never had a thorough mathematical training, or a comfortable post with undisturbed leisure in which he could give sustained attention to one topic, but lived intellectually from hand to mouth, pouring out inventions and ideas, from watch-springs to the first proposal for artificial silk, for a pittance from the Royal Society, and fees from a multitude of consulting jobs as engineer and architect.

Hooke began to insinuate that Newton had borrowed many of his leading ideas on light from him. In those days, so soon after the Civil War, and the struggle between Catholicism and Reformation, the habits of controversy were still very violent. As Newton had grown up during the Civil War, it might have been expected that he would have been used to unconsidered language and violent arguments, but under criticism he closed like a sensitive plant. He even intimated to the Royal Society that he wished to resign from its fellowship, and was with difficulty persuaded to withdraw his resignation.

There were other motives, besides sensitiveness, for this reaction. He was devoting more and more attention to theology and alchemy. He was a religious mystic with a protestant hatred of Catholicism, and attacked with passionate intensity what he conceived to be the intellectual foundations of the Roman Church. His alchemical experiments were aimed at the transmutation of base metals into gold, and the discovery of the elixir of life.

In the early years of his professorship, Newton was deep in these esoteric studies. We have already heard that in his conversations with More, his face shone with prophetic joy. The Royal Society tried with difficulty to wheedle further physical researches out of him. Hooke became Secretary of the Society in 1679, and mastered himself sufficiently to write a polite diplomatic letter, asking for further scientific news, and especially for his opinion on the attractive forces which might cause ' the celestial motions of the planets '.

Newton wrote a long and rather sarcastic reply, saying that for the last half year he had been in Lincolnshire 'cumbered with concerns' among his relations. He had had no time for philosophical meditations, and had been entirely engaged in 'country affairs'. 'And before that, I had for some years last been endeavouring to bend myself from philosophy to other studies' so much that he 'grutched' the time that he spent on science, except as a 'diversion' at 'idle hours'.

After snubbing Hooke and the Royal Society, he proceeded to 'sweeten his answer' as he later put it, by adding ' a fancy of my own about discovering the earth's diurnal motion ' (proving the earth's rotation). Then he discussed what would happen if a bullet were dropped from a great height and could fall through the earth without resistance.

He drew a figure suggesting that it would fall in a spiral curve, ending at the centre of the earth.

Hooke, Wren, Flamsteed and the other leaders of the Royal Society discussed this idea with enthusiasm, and Hooke jubilantly pointed out that Newton had made an elementary mistake. The bullet would not spiral to the centre, but would sweep round it in an ellipse.

The effect on Newton of this simple correction by the detested Hooke was stupendous. No doubt one cause of the slip was his psychological complex against Hooke, so that in the very moment of patronizing him, he made his grossest error. It was probably a Freudian mistake.

Newton was stung to the quick. He was shaken to the very depths of his being. Such reactions are not uncommon among great scholars who have received small corrections. Schuster has described how he once called on Helmholtz, who, after being the greatest physiologist on the continent of Europe, moved over to physics, and became its greatest physicist. Someone had pointed out a small error in one of his works, and Helmholtz was seated at his desk in deep depression, moaning that his scientific reputation was in ruins. The great Frazer, the meticulous author of the *Golden Bough*, once received an intimation that a misquotation had been detected in his huge masterpiece. He at once offered to resign his fellowship of Trinity College.

Newton tore himself from the delights of alchemy and the *Apocalypse* and angrily solved one of the most important problems in all science. He showed, in effect, that if a planet moved round the sun in an elliptical orbit, then the gravitational force between the planet and sun must be inversely proportional to the square of the distance. He kept the solution to himself, and put it in a drawer.

Meanwhile, Hooke, Wren and Halley continued their

discussions. One day in 1684, they were in an inn, still arguing about gravitation. Hooke claimed that he could prove the motion must be according to the inverse square law, but refused to reveal his proof. Thereupon, ' Sir Christopher, to encourage the enquiry,' offered a book prize worth ' forty shillings ' to anyone who would bring him a solution within two months.

After further unsuccessful struggles, Halley went to Cambridge in August 1684, to consult Newton, and was told that he had solved the problem several years ago. Newton tried to lay his hand on the papers, but had lost them. He set out to repeat his proof, but was held up for some time by an elementary error in his diagram of an ellipse. After he had corrected this, he stayed in Cambridge for the rest of the summer, and began working out a connected account of his discoveries, to serve as his university lectures in the autumn term. Newton sent a copy of them to Halley, who at once recognized their superlative importance. He bent all his talents to persuading Newton to prepare them for publication, and thus helped to bring forth the greatest of all scientific books : the *Principia Mathematica Philosophiae Naturalis* (the *Mathematical Principles of Natural Philosophy*).

Newton was unable to co-operate with any scientist on the basis of equality, but he could be helpful with younger men of high intelligence and tact. Halley dwelt on the necessity of his writing out his discoveries for publication, in order that he should secure to himself the priority.

Newton began on the final writing of the *Principia*, and completed it in fifteen working months. It was the intensest exhibition of intellectual effort ever seen in the history of the human race.

He deduced the general movements of material bodies in the heavens and on the earth from three laws. Philosophically, mathematically, scientifically, it was a prodigy. It contains hundreds of solutions of physical problems, including many of the most difficult and beautiful in the whole of science. It was written in Latin and cast in the severe form of classical geometry.

On its inscrutable face, like that of a gigantic sphinx, there was little hint of how he had originally found out all these things. He had used the vulgar new algebraical geometry, and his own parvenu calculus, but he had carefully erased most of the traces of these from his proofs, which he transcribed into classical geometry. One of the reasons why he did this was, perhaps, because he had an intuition, which was correct, that the new algebraical methods were not as logically rigorous as the old geometry. The calculus was not made logically rigorous until the nineteenth century. He also seemed inclined to believe that geometry was closer than algebra to the reality of solid objects in the external world. It appealed not only to number but also to the visual imagination. The work was profoundly awe-inspiring and difficult.

We have an account of what his life was like when he was writing the *Principia*. In 1685 Newton had written to the headmaster of his old school at Grantham, asking him to recommend a young man who could serve as his assistant and amanuensis. One Humphrey Newton was recommended to him, and served him in this capacity from 1685 until 1690. The copy of the manuscript of the *Principia* which was supplied to Halley was in Humphrey Newton's handwriting.

Many years later, after Newton's death, he was asked to record his reminiscences of this period. He wrote that ' his carriage then was very meek, sedate, and humble, never seemingly angry, of profound thought, his countenance mild, pleasant, and comely. I cannot say I ever saw him laugh but once'. (Newton had a charming smile, but laughed very rarely. One of the few authenticated instances was when he asked a friend, to whom he had lent a copy of Euclid, how he was progressing, and how he liked that author. His friend answered 'by desiring to know what use and benefit in life that study would be to him. Upon which Sir Isaac was very merry'.)

Humphrey Newton recorded that he kept very close to his studies, very rarely went visiting, and had few visitors. He never saw him take any exercise or recreation. He received his few foreign visitors with ' a great deal of freedom, candour, and respect'. On the rare occasions when he returned an invitation to dinner, he did it 'very handsomely, and with much satisfaction to himself'. His guests were usually masters of colleges. He never went to bed until two or three in the morning, and sometimes not until six. He never stayed in bed more than four or five hours, especially in spring and autumn, 'at which times he used to employ about six weeks in his laboratory, the fire scarcely going out either night or day; he sitting up one night and I another, till he had finished his chemical experiments . . . What his aim might be I was not able to penetrate into, but his pains, his diligence at these set times made me think he aimed at something beyond the reach of human art and industry . . .'

Newton was making all these chemical efforts in *addition* to his unparalleled exertions on the *Principia*. It looks as if he believed he was on the track of the secret of life. He had found the secret of the operations of the material universe. If he had succeeded in this, why not in that?

Newton's tendency to regard the universe and life as difficult riddles which could nevertheless be solved was not unlike Francis Bacon's attitude. Newton was very much influenced by Bacon, but owing to his habit of not recording his indebtedness, this has probably been much under-estimated. Bacon's project for the development of science was based on the belief that all problems of the universe and life were comparatively simple, though perhaps very subtle. He believed that an organized and determined effort by scientists might solve all fundamental problems, including that of the secret of immortality, within a human generation, that is, within about thirty years. Newton's notions on matter and atoms owed much to Bacon, and he also left a paper on the reorganization of the Royal Society, to fit it better for systematic discovery, evidently inspired by his own experience and Bacon's *New Atlantis*. Characteristically, the existence of this paper has generally been ignored.

Humphrey Newton went on to say that in his time, Newton rarely went to dine in hall, and then would often go in 'with shoes down at heels, stockings untied, surplice on, and his head scarcely combed'.

He kept taking a turn down the stairs into his little garden, which he had kept in very strict order, 'not enduring to see a weed in it'. After walking around the pattern of square beds, he would from time to time rush up to his study, and standing at his desk, note some new point before he troubled to sit down.

When he got up in the morning, he often forgot to complete his dressing, and sat on the edge of his bed in profound meditation for long periods, without moving. He frequently forgot his dinner, and as he had no cats or dogs, this was often left uneaten on his table. It made him very popular with his bed-maker. This was a formidable woman named Deborah, who in later years acquired prestige in Trinity by retailing anecdotes of her experiences.

Humphrey Newton recorded his master's frequent and great generosity, especially to his relatives. This makes Newton's attitude towards the cost of publication of the *Principia* all the more striking. He allowed Halley, who was then a junior and a poor man, while he himself was senior and comfortably off, to bear the whole of the expenses. He even wrote to Halley, during the process of printing, referring to the *Principia* as ' your book ', that is, as the property of Halley. The unique masterpiece, almost disowned by its author, was published in 1687.

While all this was going on, Newton was developing relations in quite another direction. In 1678 a brilliant youth, a poor younger son of a noble family, Charles Montague, had entered Trinity as an undergraduate. He made great progress in logic and the classics, and after reading Descartes' mathematical theory of the universe, he turned to the new conceptions being expounded by Newton.

Montague was eighteen years younger than Newton. He had great social gifts, and was naturally master of the ways of the world. Newton became deeply attached to him, and made him one of his very few intimate friends. No doubt the extreme contrast of their two personalities, together with certain common interests, became a bond between them. Young Montague knew how to handle exalted persons and distinguished seniors, and Newton was delighted to be acquainted with a young nobleman who was sufficiently intelligent and instructed to understand him. Montague became a fellow of Trinity, and joined Newton in an attempt to found a ' Philosophical Society of Cambridge ', but it was unsuccessful.

Montague had a facility for composing light verse. When Charles II died, he wrote a eulogistic ode about the late king, which made him the talk of London. When James II ascended the throne, Dryden, the leading poet of the age, became a Roman Catholic, and devoted a long poem to his new religion. Montague and Matthew Prior lampooned this effort. Most of the lampoon was written by Prior, but Montague got most of the credit for it. He immediately became one of the leaders of the Whigs. He resigned his fellowship at Trinity in the year after the publication of the *Principia*, and became a member of the Parliament of 1689, at the age of twenty-eight.

Montague was a brilliant debater, with a *flair* for finance. He became the spokesman of the financial magnates who came into power after the fall of James II in 1688. It is a striking fact that Newton's *Principia* was published at virtually the same time as the British financial classes first came to power, and began to give English society the characteristic features it has retained ever since.

Montague became Chancellor of the Exchequer in 1694, at the age of thirty-three, and established the Bank of England. He was a member of the Junto, the group which led the Whig revolution. He put through various sharp financial manoeuvres, and when the Tories, after their first defeats with the fall of James II, began to rally the more conservative forces, they impeached him. But by then he was in the House of Lords, as Lord Halifax, and the majority of his fellow-peers stood by him, so the impeachment failed.

As Montague grew in power he became absorbed in administration, business and intrigue, pulling all the strings, and especially patronizing writers. He was short in stature and stood on his toes to increase his height, and was derided by his opponents as a 'jackanapes', and the 'Filcher', The Tories hated him.

> Proud as Apollo on his forked hill,
> Sat full-blown Bufo, puff'd by every quill.

wrote Pope. The great Duchess of Marlborough hissed: ' he was so great a manager that when he dined alone he eat upon pewter for fear of lessening the value of his plate by cleaning it often ', and ' he was as renowned for ill-breeding as Sir Robert Walpole is '.

But this was the man who was Newton's intimate friend. Montague probably gave Newton much encouragement during the desperate period of his composition of the *Principia*. One cannot help wondering whether Newton's frantic alchemical researches, which were largely concerned with trying to transmute base metals into gold, were one of the bonds of interest between the two men. One wanted to make gold, the other to manipulate it. Montague may have had a wild hope that Newton was about to discover a secret which would enable them, in partnership, to become masters of the world.

Newton's association with Montague after the publication of the *Principia* has received general attention, but it is quite possible that their association before that event was more significant.

The *Principia* opens with a discussion of the nature of mechanics. Newton represents it as the science of the motions of material objects in the real external world. Geometry is founded on mechanical practice and is an abstraction from experience with material things. Science is not the same as manual practice, or technology, but something which has been drawn out of it, and will describe any kind of motion that can occur in the material world.

Newton regarded the science of the *Principia* as the key to all operations in material nature. Thus it became the key to the use of material things for human benefit, and the basis for a scientific civilization. The social importance of the *Principia* was at least as great as its intellectual distinction.

The whole work contains about a quarter of a million words, and is divided into three books. In the first, he completes Galileo's work on the laws of motion, and expresses it in the modern form which has enabled it to be used to solve most of the practical tasks of the machine age.

In the second book he analyzed the complex problems of the motions of bodies in resistant media. He had been led to this in order to dispose of Descartes' theory of the universe, as a system of vortices in some kind of medium. He worked out how a solid body could move in a gas or a liquid, and from his results concluded that the planets must be free from any kind of resisting medium. But incidentally, he founded the mathematical theory of gases and liquids. He showed that Boyle's law, which states that when the pressure of a mass of gas is doubled its volume is halved, could be deduced from the conception of a gas as a collection of elastic atoms. His mathematical analysis of the effect of pressure on gases led him to calculate the speed of sound-waves. He incidentally gave the first mathematical treatment of wave motion. He was fond of confirming his result by timing the famous echo which can be heard in Neville's Court at Trinity College.

His analysis of the motion of bodies in fluids led to the foundation of the science of hydrodynamics. He even gave the shape of the body of least resistance for going through a liquid, and conceived that it might 'be of use in the building of ships'. He gave no immediate hint of how he had discovered it, but in order to solve it he must have known the principles of the calculus of variations, which was not re-discovered until a hundred years later, by Lagrange.

He transformed the knowledge of gases and liquids from empiricism to a mathematical science. He provided the forthcoming age of steam and machinery with its basic theory.

These first two books of the *Principia* were at least as

important as the third, which was more spectacular and contained his astounding account of the mechanics of the heavens. He revealed the whole operations of the known cosmos as a system of attracting and revolving bodies, almost like an all-comprehending cosmical watch, in which every little movement and rotation could be calculated down to the finest detail.

The effect of this on the imagination was staggering. Hitherto the universe had been regarded as a vague, palpitating, mysterious object. Now it was revealed as operating according to known laws, so that every little feature of it could be precisely calculated.

The whole universe was brought under the subordination of the human intellect, so that the mind of man seemed suddenly to be enormously extended, and raised in dignity. It strengthened the confidence in human powers, and contributed to the optimism which characterized the Age of Reason, and helped to inspire the French Revolution and the rise of modern scientific civilization.

No wonder Newton appeared to his contemporaries as almost superhuman. Incidentally, his researches on the tides and on the measurement of time helped the maritime development of the British nation. He became an important adviser of the Government on these questions, and even proposed something like modern operational research for the practical solution of marine problems. Just as Britain sent scientists to sea to solve the submarine menace in the Second World War, so Newton advised ' that if instead of sending the observations of seamen to able mathematicians at land, the land would send able mathematicians to sea, it would signify much more to the improvement of navigation and safety of men's lives and estates on that element'.

One of the most striking features of the *Principia* is the absence of a sense of history. There is no hint in its propositions that the universe has a history, and has passed through an evolution. He regarded the universe as a machine, created by God in the beginning, and in essentials running unchanged for ever. This static view was perhaps associated with a conception of the universe as a puzzle, that contained a definite number of parts, which could be fitted together if only one could find the key.

The conception was really set for him by the general conditions of his time. The steam engine had not yet been invented, so the basic facts of the transformation of energy, of heat into mechanical work, were not yet known and were not available for him to investigate. The characteristic machine of his time was the watch, or a small water wheel or windmill. The steam engine with its promise of ever-increasing and unlimited power was not present to suggest to his imagination the idea of growth and development.

In this, Newton was a man of his time, both scientifically and technologically. Whole aspects of phenomena had been withheld from his scrutiny, because science and technology in general had not yet advanced to the stage at which they had become explicit.

The same absence of a sense of history is seen in Newton's large volume on *Chronology*. He accepted the current belief that the creation occurred about 4000 B.C., and on that assumption, he constructed a table of dates, made to 'suit with the course of nature, with astronomy, with sacred history, with Herodotus the Father of History, and with itself . . .' He fitted the history of the world into a brief six thousand years, apparently without a qualm. And yet, for all that, he recorded speculations which show amazing prescience into twentieth century ideas, though of course there was not yet a sufficient body of evidence to support them.

Immediately after the publication of the *Principia* Newton was involved in the forefront of politics. The University elected him to represent it in Parliament at the time of the rebellion against James II. He wrote a very important letter to the Vice-Chancellor of the University, in which he defined the new Whig doctrine of limited allegiance to the King. He said that allegiance was due to the king in fact, and that it was 'treason to be in arms against a king *de facto* tho' it be in behalf of a king *de jure*', a very convenient philosophy for a rebel!

This letter justifying rebellion against James II is written in the same magisterial style as the *Principia*.

When James II came to the throne, he attempted to force the University of Cambridge to give a Catholic monk a degree by Royal mandate. It was evident that if the University acquiesced, first the University, and then the Church would gradually be catholicized, and finally all England. Newton was a member of the University delegation summoned to appear before the terrible judge Jeffries to explain why the monk should not be admitted. The leader of the delegation broke down under Jeffries' brow-beating, and would have compromised, had not Newton rallied the delegation during an adjournment. As a result, the delegation recovered its morale, and refused to compromise.

So James II, the pale imitation of Pope Urban VIII who had persecuted Galileo, was first halted by no other person than Newton himself. The difference in the experiences of Galileo and Newton shows how much easier the path of science had become.

After his prodigious mental labours Newton seemed to experience a revulsion against the Cambridge academic life. It would have indeed been surprising if he had not felt tired, and in need of a change.

His friendship with Montague, and his quite important participation in politics, no doubt whetted his taste for a place in the great world of affairs. The publication of the *Principia* brought him a great prestige, and a wider acquaintance. He became friendly with the philosopher John Locke. He solicited Montague, his junior and former pupil, and Locke, for a government appointment. Newton keenly desired to raise his social position. His solicitations were impelled by various motives, and, as was his habit when he began to direct his mind towards any thing, it tended to become a fixed idea. Unfortunately, Montague could not satisfy him immediately. Newton made himself very agreeable to Locke who had influential connections among the more moderate Whigs. But Locke also was not able to find a place for him at once.

In his condition of fatigue and frustration, Newton had a nervous breakdown. It was probably also accelerated by the death of his mother, to whom he had been deeply attached.

He began to complain of sleeplessness and failing appetite, and evidently suffered from delusions of persecution. He wrote to Locke that Montague had become ' false ' to him, and he abjectly asked Locke to beg Lord Monmouth's pardon, ' for pressing into his company the last time I saw him '. Then Samuel Pepys was dumbfounded by the reception of an incoherent letter, in which Newton said that he had never tried to get anything through the influence of Pepys or King James, and must in future withdraw from his acquaintance.

Three days later, Newton wrote to Locke, accusing him of attempts to ' embroil ' him ' with women ', and told him that when he heard that he was sick he had commented that it would be better if he were dead. Locke wrote a very kind remonstrance, and then continued his letter as if nothing had happened. Newton wrote to Locke shortly afterwards, saying that he had been ill, and had slept ' for five nights together not a wink'. Years later, Locke recorded that Newton was 'a nice man to deal with ', in the sense of being touchy and difficult.

The wonder is not that Newton broke down, but that his breakdown did not come earlier. The plunge straight from the *Principia* into the excitement of a political rebellion indeed exposed him to an enormous strain.

The experienced Pepys sent his friend Millington to see Newton, who at once told him that he had been troubled with 'a distemper that much seized his head '. Millington reported that he now seemed well, but melancholy, and remarked that it was very unfortunate that ' such a person as Newton lies so neglected by those in power '.

While Newton recovered the external appearance of health he was never the same man again. His nervous irritability, and overbearing disposition, increased. He was plainly bored with his old Cambridge life, and wanted to get away to the great city.

He had left a portion of the *Principia* dealing with the motion of the moon unfinished. But as it was of great importance for navigation, he was urged to proceed with it. The difficulties of lunar theory are very great, and taxed mathematical theory as then developed to the very limit. Newton bent his mighty mind to it, and made extraordinary progress. But it was too much, even for him. A further hundred years of world progress in mathematics was necessary before it could be worked out tolerably completely. Newton said that the problem of the moon was the only one that had ever made his head ache.

He needed the exact observations of the position of the moon made by the Astronomer Royal, Flamsteed, for the working out of the theory. He considered that it was Flamsteed's duty to supply them, and demanded them of him as if he were one of his personal servants.

The distinguished Flamsteed furiously resented this. Newton used his prestige to force Flamsteed to give him the data. The conflict with Hooke was repeated with Flamsteed. These were merely internal English quarrels, but an even more momentous one developed with the great Leibnitz, over the invention of the calculus. This occupied much of Newton's attention during the latter part of his life.

Meanwhile, however, Newton's friends had at last found him a place. Montague had acquired power, and in 1696 offered him the post of Warden of the Mint.

Montague was engaged in financial reforms which were laying the foundations of the modern British commercial state. After the turmoil of the Civil War the coinage was severely corrupted and a recoinage was essential as a stable basis for the new development of commerce. But the carrying out of the recoinage was a delicate matter. In the general atmosphere of corruption, the official responsible would be exposed to exceptional dangers of bribery. A capable person of rigid honesty was required. Montague chose Newton for the job.

One of Newton's first tasks as Warden of the Mint was the apprehension of counterfeiters. He entered into every aspect of these police activities, compiling case-books, having himself made a justice of the peace, and interviewing criminals and solicitors personally. He supplied his agents with gentleman's clothes as disguises to aid them in their detective work. He successfully caught the wealthy counterfeiter Challoner, who was backed by a group of influential politicians, which was no mean feat for the ex-don.

He pursued his task with cold efficiency, and when consulted years later whether a counterfeiter who had been convicted should be hung, he replied that he was ' humbly of the opinion that it's better to let him suffer ', for ' these people very seldom leave off '.

Newton's life-long habit of attention to accounts and property now served him well. He proved a capable administrator, in the manner of a senior civil servant. On occasion, he was asked for advice on currency policy. He flirted with the idea of a managed paper currency, but came down in practice on the conventional metal type. The activity which has most impressed his professional successors at the Mint was his personal investigation of methods of assaying metals. He mastered the chemical and metallurgical technique with his own hands, but he did not introduce any scientifically improved processes.

Newton had been comfortably off at Cambridge, but at the Mint he became a rich man. His income there rose, from salary and perquisites, to more than £2000 a year by the end of his life. This enabled him to live in a well-to-do style, and practise widespread generosity among his friends and numerous relatives. He saved a large fortune, which amounted to about £32,000. At the time of his death, his total income from the Mint, and the interest on his investments, was about £4000 a year. He had invested £10,000 in the South Sea Company which, up to 1720, had made large profits out of the slave trade. Then it became the instrument of the most notorious wave of financial speculation in British history, the South Sea Bubble. Newton retained his holdings throughout the boom, and lost heavily. He was not a speculator.

Newton's half-sister Hannah had married a poor clergyman called Barton, and had several children, one of whom was an attractive girl named Catherine. He helped the family by becoming responsible for her education. When he moved to London, he virtually adopted her. She was probably about sixteen then, and soon became the domestic manager of his household. She grew into one of the most beautiful and witty women of the period, the subject of three of Dryden's poems, and the toast of the Kit-Cat Club, the meeting-place of Montague and the Whig leaders.

Under the benign eye of her august uncle, Catherine's drawing-room became the centre of London fashion. Newton was delighted to observe that the most exalted young noblemen vied with each other to secure invitations to his house. For his part, he withdrew from the lively company as quickly as was polite, and went to his own rooms, where he usually had his meals by himself, and then engaged in his interminable meditations on the riddle of the universe. As he became older and less confident, his interest in the sublime problems seems to have declined into a taste for any kind of arithmetical or chronological puzzle. It has been said that if he had lived in our times, he would have become addicted to crossword puzzles and detective stories.

The great Montague became devoted to Catherine. After the death of his wife, she moved over from her uncle's house to his, in the capacity of 'superintendent of his domestic affairs'. When Montague died nine years later, he left £5000 to Catherine Barton, with Bushy Park (now the headquarters of the National Physical Laboratory) and rents to keep it in good repair.

Such events did not pass without comment. The gossip-writer of the day, one Mrs. Manley, retailed the debaucheries of Montague, disguised as fiction in the manner of *Quo Vadis*? Montague, in the figure of Sergius, is asked: 'What has become of the charming Bartica?', and answers with sobs: 'She's a traitress, an inconsistent proud baggage, yet I love her dearly, and have lavished myriads upon her, besides getting her worthy ancient parent a good post for connivance . . .'

When Voltaire visited London, and became the chief

propagandist in Europe of the new Newtonian science, he met Catherine Barton. He later reported that he had thought in his youth that Newton had received his appointment at the Mint through extreme merit. 'Not at all. Isaac Newton had a most charming niece . . . she greatly pleased the Chancellor of the Exchequer . . . The infinitesimal calculus would have been of no assistance to him without a pretty niece.'

Dates prove that Mrs. Manley and Voltaire were wrong in their insinuation of how Newton got his appointment, but there seems no reasonable doubt that Catherine Barton became Montague's mistress, and that Newton was fully aware of the situation. After Montague's death, Catherine rather plaintively returned to her old position in her uncle's house. Two years later, she married the well-to-do John Conduitt. They lived with Newton and looked after him until the end of his life.

The Conduitt's daughter had a son who succeeded to the title of the Earl of Portsmouth. Through this relationship the Portsmouth family inherited Newton's papers. In 1936 many of them were sold. The late Lord Keynes, 'disturbed by this impiety,' managed to buy about half of them back. His studies of Newton's alchemical writings led him to the conclusion that Newton had tried to be a magician. Newton's intense absorption in an attempt to find the philosopher's stone has a Faustian resonance: ' 'Tis magic, magic that has ravished me . . .' Just as he concealed what he called his 'mystic fancies' in religion, so he concealed his necromantic passion. Both were out of tune with the growing rationalism of the age, so he buried them under a cover of secrecy.

In his papers he noted that the secret of the transmutation of mercury seemed to have been concealed, and he commented that it 'therefore may possibly be an inlet to something more noble not to be communicated without immense danger to the world '. Like the modern physicists who make atomic and hydrogen bombs, he was concerned with problems of security.

An important new insight into Newton's chemical ideas was obtained in 1946, when the late S. I. Vavilov showed that he had propounded a nuclear theory of the atom, and had suggested that ordinary chemical changes depend on the outer part of the atom, while transmutations of one element into another depend on changes in its nucleus. He had foreseen something like Rutherford's atom and the modern atomic transmutation.

Newton's London life was in striking contrast with his former Cambridge life. In his later years, his post at the Mint was largely a sinecure.

After the hated Hooke had died in 1703, Newton accepted the Presidency of the Royal Society, and published his *Optics*, which had existed in manuscript for about thirty years. He presided at the Royal Society with great regularity. The weekly meeting day was changed to Thursday to meet his convenience, on which it has remained ever since.

He used the Royal Society to conduct his controversies with Flamsteed, and with Leibnitz on the invention of the calculus. Leibnitz had invented it independently and later, but had published it first. Newton's friends insinuated that Leibnitz had stolen the idea from Newton. As Newton grew older he seemed to accept this view himself, and the question also became one of national prestige.

The Royal Society issued documents, drafted under Newton's closest supervision, purporting to prove that Leibnitz had acquired the idea from Newton. Leibnitz replied with anonymous documents, containing the reverse insinuations. Newton's disciples referred to Leibnitz and his friends as those 'Leipzig rogues'. Leibnitz's notation for the calculus was easier to use, so that the new pure mathematics developed more quickly on the Continent, where the leadership in this subject has remained ever since. The uncritical adulation of Newton became a brake on the progress of pure mathematics in England.

In London, Newton did not pursue any scientfic investigation unless stimulated by some specific demand. He lost the zest for scientific research, but not the ability.

In 1696 John Bernoulli proposed the problem of finding the curve along which a body will fall in the shortest time, from one point to another, below and away from it. Leibnitz solved it after six months' effort, and suggested it should be sent to Newton as a challenge.

Newton found it waiting for him, on arriving home at four o'clock in the afternoon from the Mint. By four o'clock in the following morning he had got it out. He published the solution anonymously, but when Bernoulli read it, he at once recognized the author from its style; '*Tanquam ex ungue leonem*', it had the mark of the lion's paw.

Newton wrote snootily to Flamsteed: ' I do not love to be printed upon every occasion, much less to be dunned and teased by foreigners about mathematical things, or to be thought by our own people to be trifling away my time about them, when I should be about the King's business . . .'

Newton was knighted by Queen Anne in 1705, in the Master's Lodge of Trinity College. He was the first scientist to receive this honour for his achievements as such.

He died in 1727, and was buried in Westminster Abbey. His pall was carried to the grave by dukes and earls.

He left no will. His fortune was divided between his nephews and nieces. His heir-at-law, a dissolute agricultural labourer, inherited his Woolsthorpe manor, and died through swallowing a clay-pipe, which broke in his throat during a drunken orgy. Apart from his mother and Catherine Barton, Newton's numerous relatives seem to have been below the average in intelligence and character.

The inventory of his effects was discovered about thirty years ago. It is on a scroll five inches wide and seventeen feet long. It gives a complete list of the contents of his house, which was in St. Martin's Lane off Leicester Square, where the Westminster Public Library now stands. It shows that when Newton died, he had very few valuables. There were only four buckets for the ablutions of the whole household. His clothes, including his silver-hilted sword, were valued at £8. He had only two suits. He had a penchant for crimson plush upholstery.

The oddest of Newton's furnishings were two solid silver chamber vessels. In his day, these were kept near to the dining room, convenient for the gentlemen at their wine, after the ladies had withdrawn. The inventory suggests that Newton spent very little on himself and followed a simple regimen, except when he entertained. Then he left orders for dinners in this fashion : ' Fish. Pasty. Fricassy of chickens and a dish of puddens. Quarter lamb. Wild fowl. Peas and Lobsters '.

Newton started his scientific career by ruthlessly pruning away from his work all unproved speculations. *Hypotheses non fingo*, I do not deal in hypotheses, he said. But during his life he noted those speculations which seemed to him to contain essential truth, though he could not prove it, and then published them at the ends of his books. He finished the second book of the second edition published in 1713, of the *Principia*, with a marvellous speculation, in which he attributed the chemical combinations of atoms to electrical forces, and the functioning of the muscles to electrical influences propagated along the nerves. This was a hundred years before the electric current was discovered. He gave a collection of many others, equally extraordinary, at the end of his *Optics*.

He foreshadowed the discovery of the transmutation of particles into radiations, and radiations into particles. He sketched a picture of the structure of inorganic and organic substances, very much like that revealed by modern chemistry and physics. He saw that ' the variety of motion in the world was always decreasing ', and in those words seemed to be stretching towards one of the fundamental ideas of modern thermo-dynamics.

He saw that the system of the universe and the conditions that make life possible depend on the heat or energy derived from gravitation and other principles, which kept the sun shining, and without which all would freeze and grow cold, and ' Life would cease '.

When Newton was asked how his genius differed from that of other men, he replied that he believed that he had a greater power of concentration. He could hold a problem in his mind with more sustained intensity, until all the parts fell into place, and the solution appeared to him.

He owed his achievements to sheer hard thinking, and did not require discussion with others. There have been other very great scientists, such as Faraday, who had no collaborators.

Einstein has said that Newton ' stands before us strong, certain, and alone : his joy in creation and his minute precision are evident in every word and in every figure '.

Newton's attitude to science and life grew directly out of the conditions of his day. He was an individualistic Englishman, with a strong sense of property both in science and goods. He considered it was entirely for him to say what he should do with his own. He believed that he had the right to keep his discoveries and opinions to himself, if he wished. He did not consider that, in return for the opportunities given him by society, he was bound to give society the fruits of his investigations. He was prepared to mind his own business, and he expected other people to mind theirs. He acknowledged no debts to teachers, contemporaries, university, or country. His champions represented his reticence as modesty, and his enemies as hypocrisy.

The extraordinary way in which his personality developed, so that it did not fit in with any preconceived ideas of science and social life may perhaps be best understood from Wordsworth's description in the *Prelude* of the Cambridge dons:

Of the Grave Elders, men unscoured, grotesque
In character, tricked out like aged trees
Which through the lapse of their infirmity
Give ready place to any random seed
That chooses to be reared upon their trunks . . .

Newton was the result, when a seed of unparalleled genius chose to fall upon the Cambridge evironment after the Civil War.

He spent virtually the whole of his life in Woolsthorpe, Cambridge, and London. He did not visit Oxford until he was seventy-eight, and there is no record of his having made any kind of tour, nor did he ever go out of England.

By virtue of the magnitude and importance of his published work, Newton is the greatest scientist who ever lived. But much remains to be learned before his mind and soul can be fully understood.

REFERENCES

Isaac Newton, by L. T. More. Scribner: 1934.
The Social and Economic Roots of Newton's Principia, by B. Hessen. Kniga: 1931.

Newton: The Man, by R. de Villamil. Knox: 1931.

Newton Tercentenary Celebrations, The Royal Society. Cambridge University Press: 1947.

Newton at the Mint, by John Craig. Cambridge University Press: 1946.

CHARLES DARWIN
1809 -1882

AFTER Newton had shown, by means of the law of gravitation, that all the material universe could be conceived as one precisely operating machine, it was natural to look for a comparable unifying idea in the world of living organisms.

This was found by Charles Darwin, in his Theory of Evolution. He showed that all living organisms are related members of one connected system. Each is, as it were, a single branch on one great tree of life.

Charles Robert Darwin was born at Shrewsbury on February 12th, 1809. His paternal ancestors are first heard of, like Newton's, as small Lincolnshire farmers. They were promoted by the Stuarts and fought for them, one becoming Recorder of the City of Lincoln after the Restoration. Darwin's great-grandfather was an acquaintance of Stukeley, Isaac Newton's friend. He was a capable botanist who published an introduction to *Linnaeus*, which ran into three editions. His seventh child was Erasmus Darwin, one of the most remarkable figures of the eighteenth century, and grandfather of Charles.

Erasmus Darwin was born in 1731. He became a stout, strong, clumsy man of immense physical and mental vitality. He was interested in almost everything, except field sports, and already when a boy was industriously writing verse, making mechanical contrivances, and trying the new electrical experiments which were becoming fashionable. He gained a scholarship at St. John's College, Cambridge,

137

where he prepared for the study of medicine. After graduating, he went to Edinburgh, where he became friendly with the chemist James Keir, and 'sacrificed to both Bacchus and Venus'. He found that this was too much for his health, so he cut Bacchus out.

While he was at Edinburgh, his father died, and in reflecting on his loss remarked that while he believed in the existence of a God who had created the world, he did not believe that God interposed in particular affairs. He was following Newton's conception of a universe governed by law, and not requiring the interposition of the Almighty after it had been created. Already the ascendancy of the rule of scientific law over divine intervention was being established in the Darwinian tradition.

After he had qualified, he set up in practice at Lichfield, where he was an immediate success. His income rose steadily, and after 1770 was never less than £1000 a year. In spite of a bad stutter he gained the confidence of his patients, through the strength of his personality and charm, and variety of knowledge. He worked out for himself theories of medicine which were in advance of his day, and gave more weight to psychological factors, and their interaction with physical conditions.

He married soon after settling in Lichfield, and his wife quickly produced five children. She died early, being worn out by 'the frequency of her maternal situation'. Their third son, Robert Waring Darwin, was the father of Charles Darwin.

Erasmus Darwin soon became the most eminent doctor in the Midlands. As such he was consulted by the great figures of the Industrial Revolution, such as Matthew Boulton and Josiah Wedgwood. Besides giving them medical advice, he entered with them into the new spirit of practical scientific progress, searching and speculating in every direction for scientific knowledge which could be turned to industrial profit.

He designed a special carriage, in which he made his long rides to distant patients. It was fitted with various conveniences for study, so that he could utilize every minute of his journeys, and make immediate notes on his readings and meditations. There was room for one person only, in order to protect him from the intrusion of travelling companions. It is surprizing that he could do so much in a bumping, shaking carriage, but he composed innumerable verses, and compiled an immense number of notes on all kinds of things, medical observations, sleep, sanitation, pure water supplies, submarines, a rotary pump, a machine which could say ' Mama ', a horizontal windmill, and hundreds of other things. He had a speaking tube in his house, with which he scared the servants. He proposed a locomotive steam engine to Boulton before the latter had met James Watt. He foresaw the future :

> Soon shall they arm, Unconquered Steam! afar
> Drag the slow barge, or drive the rapid car;
> Or on wide-waving wings expanded bear
> The flying chariot through the fields of air.
> —Fair crews triumphant, leaning from above,
> Shall wave their fluttering kerchiefs as they move;
> Or warrior bands alarm the gaping crowd,
> And armies shrink beneath the shadowy cloud.

Erasmus and his Birmingham friends founded the famous Lunar Society, which included among its members and visitors Boulton, James Watt, Samuel Galton, William Small who ' fixed the destinies ' of Jefferson's life, Benjamin Franklin, Thomas Day, the author of *Sandford and Merton*, Priestley, Keir and Wedgwood. It met on the nights of full moons, so that members could find their way home easily afterwards.

They were sympathetic to Rousseau. They supported the Americans in the War of Independence, and welcomed the earlier phases of the French Revolution. They were radical in politics, unitarian in religion and progressive capitalists by principle. Once, when Erasmus was unable to attend, he exclaimed: 'Lord! what inventions, what wit, what rhetoric, metaphysical, mechanical, and pyrotechnical, will be on the wing, bandied like a shuttlecock from one to another of your troupe of philosophers! while poor I, I by myself I, imprisoned in a post-chaise, am joggled, and jostled, and bumped, and bruised along the King's highroad to make war upon a stomach-ache or a fever'.

He corresponded with the geologist Hutton, who introduced the uniformitarian theory into geology, and laid the foundation of the method employed by Lyell and then by Charles Darwin himself, to revolutionize the conception of the history of the earth and living organisms. He even coped with the great Rousseau, who tried to evade meeting him while writing the *Confessions* at Wootton Hall in Staffordshire. Erasmus walked up and down the garden, outside the window of the room where Rousseau was working, staring at a plant from time to time, extremely intently. After a while, Rousseau could contain his curiosity no longer, and came into the garden to see what it was all about.

In his wide, discursive reading, Erasmus paid much attention to the works of another great Frenchman, Buffon, who had been inspired to extend Isaac Newton's description of the universe to include animate as well as inanimate things. Buffon's immense work, in forty-four volumes depicted a panorama of nature as a whole, which could scarcely fail to suggest some evolutionary ideas.

Meditating on Buffon's multitudes of facts, Erasmus commented on the remarkable changes seen in many animals after birth, such as the butterfly from the caterpillar, and air-breathing frog from the water-breathing tadpole. Great changes were produced by artificial cultivation, such as the variety of dogs, from spaniels to greyhounds, by climates which changed the coats of animals, and by crossing.

The variety was prodigious, and yet 'the similarity of structure which obtains in all the warm-blooded animals, including mankind, from the mouse and bat to the elephant and whale' led one 'to conclude that they have alike been produced from a similar living filament'.

He supposed that the original 'filament' was a sperm, and that it had changed into the whole variety of living nature through the influence of the environment, according to what was subsequently called the inheritance of acquired characters. Such were the views which Erasmus published by 1796.

Meanwhile, besides being read throughout Europe, Erasmus Darwin's reputation as a doctor had spread far. He had wished in his youth to practise in London, but chose the provinces because he feared the metropolitan competition. When he had become famous, George III said that if he would come to London he could be the King's Physician. But still he would not come. It is said that he did not wish to compete with Samuel Johnson as the most striking personality of the town, and preferred to stay in the provinces where he was undisputed king. In the end, patients from London, and from Europe, had to travel to the Midlands to secure his advice.

Erasmus had five children by his first wife, and seven by his second, besides taking over her children by her deceased first husband. In addition he had two illegitimate daughters, the Miss Parkers, by an unidentified woman of the working class. Besides supporting his legal families, he helped to establish a school conducted by the Miss Parkers, for the education of young ladies. He wrote the prospectus containing a *Plan for the Conduct of Female Education in Boarding Schools*, in which it was laid down that the girls should be trained to develop 'internal strength and activity of mind, capable to transact the business or combat the evils of life', by which 'the female character becomes complete, excites our love, and commands our admiration'. He would himself be their medical officer, and some of his young relatives would be among the pupils.

Josiah Wedgwood, who was about one year his senior, met him originally as a patient. He sought his advice early in the 1760's, and immediately became a friend. Wedgwood was one of the chief figures of the new industrialism. He added to the improved business and manufacturing methods a new standard of quality. Cheapness had been the first feature of the products of the new industry. By raising their quality and reliability, Wedgwood helped to establish it as the ruling industry of the future. He was the example of responsibility and culture among the new industrialists who were preparing to take over the leadership of the country. He allied the new business with the old traditions of the landed gentry. In his country house, life combined Arcadian pleasures with high civilization and sound business sense.

He created an industrial town for his new works, which, on the suggestion of Erasmus Darwin, was called Etruria. He made fine pottery, and exported his wares to all parts of the world. His prodigious dinner service, made for Catherine the Great, and containing 1300 views of British scenery, is still one of the greatest glories in the Kremlin Museum.

Wedgwood was authoritative, but rigidly honest and kind, according to his own principles. He communicated his conceptions to a large family of seven children, reared in freedom from financial worries, finely cultivated and disciplined.

Wedgwood's first child, Susannah, married Robert Waring Darwin in 1796, and became the mother of Charles Darwin. His fourth child, Josiah, grew up and founded another fine family society of nine children, the youngest of whom, Emma, became Charles Darwin's wife. Thus the Wedgwoods and the Darwins were bred, and then in-bred.

Robert Waring Darwin had followed his father's path, and after graduating in medicine at Leyden, set up in practice at Shrewsbury in 1787. His father assisted him to become a fellow of the Royal Society in 1788, in the same year as Lavoisier and Gibbon. He soon became the leading physician in the town, and retained that position for half a century. He was physically a very big man, with strong opinions and dominating conversation.

During the period of the Napoleonic Wars, with the high corn prices, Shrewsbury was very prosperous. The local gentry had town houses there, where they spent the winter on the social round of parties and balls. Robert Darwin soon became comfortably-off, and later on was said to enjoy a larger income from his practice than any other doctor outside London.

His wife Susannah Wedgwood, like all her sisters and brothers, inherited not less than £25,000 from her father. Robert Waring Darwin became a rich man. His wife bore him six children, of whom the fifth was Charles Robert Darwin.

Robert Waring Darwin was thirty-nine before his famous son was born. Charles recorded that his father was the most acute observer that he had ever met, and had an astonishing power of reading peoples' thoughts. He had considerable scientific knowledge. He was a good theorizer, but had little taste for scientific proof, and in Charles' view, for this reason could not be called a true scientist.

Charles grew up in awe of this big, penetrating, elderly

parent, who was dominating and read one's thoughts at a glance. His children referred to him as 'the tide', and when 'the tide came in' after his day's visits, it immediately determined the flow of activity in the house. Little Charles was quite overborne by the kind but gigantic parent.

Darwin has left us his own description of his childhood. He could remember scarcely anything of his mother, though she did not die until he was eight. She was a Unitarian, and the first school to which he was sent was conducted by a Unitarian minister.

The similarities and differences of Newton and Darwin in this connection are striking. Newton concealed his unitarianism as a terrible secret; Darwin was launched by his mother into a unitarian atmosphere at the beginning of his life. He already exhibited a passion for collecting, which ran to shells, coins, and all kinds of things, and he was given to telling fibs in order to impress his father. He was sent to Shrewsbury School under the memorable Dr. Butler, grandfather of Samuel Butler, and appreciated his life there as a boarder. But as his home was only a mile away, he would run for a short visit on almost every day. He does not seem to have shared the resentment of those unruly boys who so disliked Dr. Butler's catering that they rebelled and threw stones through the sacred windows of the Headmaster's study. Butler made so much money out of the boarders that he found his translation to the Bishopric of Lichfield inflicted on him a heavy loss of income.

Darwin said that nothing could have been worse for his mind than Dr. Butler's school. The course was strictly classical, and its effect as a means for training was for him 'simply a blank'. All his life he was unable to master any except his native language. One of the main subjects was versifying, for which he had no talent. But having many friends, he was able to patch their old verses into something that would pass muster. Butler used to make alarming hums as he studied compositions of this kind, and recognized their ancestry.

Darwin spent seven years in the school, working quite hard, but achieving no particular notice. He was rated rather below the average in intellect. His exasperated father, who was an affectionate though awe-inspiring man, said to him: 'You care for nothing but shooting, dogs, and rat-catching, and you will be a disgrace to yourself and all your family'.

Outside school-hours, however, he enjoyed being specially tutored in Euclid, and he read a good deal of poetry, especially Shakespeare's historical plays, and the poems of Scott and Byron, which had been recently published. Though, to his great regret, he lost his taste in later life for poetry, he had felt the force of the Romantic poets, and in 1822 a visit to Wales awakened his delight in scenery, which lasted longer than any other of his aesthetic pleasures.

The strongest imaginative impression of his boyhood was gained from the popular work of the day on the *Wonders of the World*. It aroused his desire to see the remote parts of the earth. This was ultimately satisfied by his voyage in the *Beagle*, during which the idea of evolution took shape in his mind.

Darwin's elder brother Erasmus was interested in chemistry. He experimented in a shed at the bottom of the garden, and allowed Charles to help. Darwin said that this was the most valuable part of his education during the period of his schooldays, for it taught him the meaning of experimental science. His schoolfellows nicknamed him 'Gas', and Dr. Butler publicly rebuked him for wasting his time on useless subjects.

As he was not receiving good reports, his father took him

away from school early, and sent him to Edinburgh before he was seventeen years old, to prepare for a medical qualification. But he gained the impression that he would ultimately inherit from his father an income which would be sufficient to live on.

Without yet fully understanding himself, his quiet but sensitive and highly-strung nature quite unfitted him for the brutal medicine of those days. He knew in his heart that it would never be really necessary for him to practise, and his revulsion was increased by the Edinburgh teaching through lectures which he found intolerably dull. He was never urged to learn dissection, and considered afterwards that the failure to master this technique, and drawing, when he was young, were two of his greatest handicaps in his later work.

Though he found the academic course dull, he was again active in personal study. He became a member of the council of the students' natural history society when he was seventeen. This brought him in close relations with the younger zoologists. He worked hard at the organisms to be found on the shore of the Firth of Forth, and in 1827, when he was eighteen, described his first two scientific discoveries. These concerned the eggs of the sea-mat found on brown seaweed, and of a leech found on the skate. This work no doubt arose out of his association with the distinguished marine zoologist, Dr. Robert Grant, who was then thirty-three years old. Grant had studied in Paris for five years after 1815, and probably had met Lamarck and become familiar with his work. Darwin used to assist Grant in collecting expeditions on the seashore, and once, when they were walking together, Grant 'burst forth in high admiration of Lamarck and his views on evolution'. Darwin 'listened in silent astonishment'. He had read similar views in his grandfather's writings, which he greatly admired at this time. Darwin always deprecated the suggestion that the ideas of his grandfather and Lamarck had much effect on him, though he did admit that his early hearing of such views being maintained and praised made it easier for him to uphold them afterwards, in a different form, in his *Origin of Species*.

Darwin had direct access to the enthusiastic atmosphere of evolutionary ideas in the formative period of his youth. His cool depreciation of this influence caused some to accuse him of trying to underrate his indebtedness to others. His attitude was, however, more probably just that of a professional scientist. Having learned of evolutionary speculations at an early age from the best sources, he took them for granted, and considered that the next step was now the important one: proving that any of them were true.

Darwin had immense speculative fertility, and like Newton had the same ruthless attitude to hypotheses. He was fed up with speculations: he wanted to prove something. In a sense, Newton and Darwin were in their respective fields the first scientists who were fully professional in spirit, and cut out all amateur speculations, however interesting and amusing. Nothing was to be admitted to the body of accepted science except that which had been decisively proved.

Darwin had already proceeded a considerable distance in his scientific development by the age of eighteen, but not in the direction of medicine. Seeing that his son's progress at Edinburgh University was as disappointing as it had been at Shrewsbury School, his father in desperation again took him away, and sent him to Cambridge, to qualify for the last refuge of a gentleman: the church.

Not having 'heard or thought' much about Church dogma, Darwin very carefully read *Pearson on the Creed,* and felt fully satisfied. He did not then 'in the least doubt the strict literal truth of every word in the Bible'. With his interest in natural history, and his passion for shooting, he rather looked forward to the idea of being a rural clergyman.

Darwin later recorded that the members of a German phrenological society, after scrutinizing one of his photographs, reported that he 'had the bump of reverence developed enough for ten priests'.

However, on looking again at the classics which he would have to study in preparation for theology, he found that he had forgotten the whole of Greek, and even some of the Greek letters. His knowledge was revived by a little special coaching, and he entered Christ's College in 1828. At the time, the college was dominated by a sporting set, with the tutor at its head. This Mr. Shaw was always happy to meet his pupils at the Newmarket race-course. Darwin practised shooting in his rooms at Christ's. He loaded his gun with a cap and aimed at a naked candle. If he shot straight, the puff from the gun blew the candle out. The tutor reported that Mr. Darwin seemed to spend hours in his rooms cracking his riding whip, and wondered.

Charles dined and wined with the sporting men, and trembled on the brink of dissipation. But one of their avocations was collecting beetles, no nonsense about science, but seeing who could obtain the largest number and variety in the shortest time. No holds were barred; one could bribe servants to assist.

Charles beat everyone hollow at this game. He invented two new methods of collecting, by scraping moss off old trees and stuffing it in a large bag, and collecting the rubbish from the bottoms of barges bringing reeds from the fens. Once, when he had torn a piece of old bark off a tree, he saw several rare species running in various directions.

He snatched them all up, but had not enough receptacles, so he stuffed one of them into his mouth for safe keeping. But it exuded an 'intensely acrid fluid', and he had to spit it out.

Darwin's memory for beetles was prodigious. When so many of the events of his early life had faded in old age, he could instantly recall the minutest details of his early prizes.

His passion for collecting was first led towards science by his cousin William Darwin Fox, who happened to be a fellow-student at Christ's. Fox introduced him to the botanist the Reverend J. S. Henslow, who in 1828 was still only thirty-two years old, and had already been six years a professor. On Friday evenings, Henslow welcomed at his house everyone interested in natural history. Seniors and juniors mingled informally, exhibiting specimens and engaging in discussion. Under Henslow's grave and tactful guidance, Darwin gradually became a trained naturalist, and by his third year had become Henslow's favourite pupil, and was generally known as 'the man who walks with Henslow'.

He presently began to think seriously about his future vocation, and asked one of his most intimate friends whether he was 'inwardly moved by the Holy Spirit'. His friend replied that he was not, and Darwin said that neither was he, and that therefore he would not be able to 'take orders'. But this was not yet a binding decision, for he was much influenced by the example of Henslow, who was very religious and would have been grieved if even 'a single word of the Thirty-nine Articles were altered'.

Darwin still had no mature scientific aims. But he made many friends. Among these was the great William Whewell, known as 'Whuffler' among undergraduates, the future Master of Trinity, of whom Sydney Smith said that science was his forte and omniscience his foible. Darwin was more and more the only junior in private expeditions of senior naturalists, and looking back on this, wrote that 'there must have been something in me a little superior to the common run of youths'.

But he found the usual course of study for the ordinary bachelor's degree very trying, especially in the last stages before the examination, which he took in 1831. Among the few things he enjoyed was Paley's *Natural Theology*, which seemed to him then to be a perfect example of logical argument. It is said that Paley was impelled to write it as a reply to the evolutionary speculations of Erasmus Darwin.

Charles was greatly relieved to find that he had done fairly well in the examination. He had, however, to spend two more terms at Cambridge to fulfil his residential qualification for a degree. Immediate anxieties were at an end, and all his time was at his disposal. He now read two books which helped to orientate his life. The first of these was Alexander von Humboldt's *Personal Narrative* of his famous travels in Central America. This fired his imagination, especially Humboldt's description of the peak of Teneriffe, which he copied out and read with such enthusiasm to Henslow and his friends that even they desired to go and see it. As for Charles, he was quite determined on it, and began enquiries with London shipping firms for a passage.

The second of the books which deeply influenced him was Sir John Herschel's *Study of Natural Philosophy*. The author dealt with the principles and aims of scientific inquiry, and represented it as an activity in which moderate abilities could do useful work. Darwin probably acquired from it the notion that professional scientific work was not above him. After his failure to pursue medicine, he was doubly troubled at the prospect of disappointing his father again by failing to enter the Church, for which in his heart he felt no call. Science began to appear as an alternative which he could reasonably propose to his father.

On the suggestion of Henslow, the eminent geologist Adam Sedgwick invited Charles to accompany him on an expedition to North Wales. One evening Charles told him of his apparently extraordinary discovery of a tropical shell in a gravel pit at Shrewsbury. Sedgwick said that it must have been thrown there, and if not, it would be one of the greatest misfortunes for geology. Charles was utterly astonished, and then for the first time fully understood that science was not merely the collecting of facts, but the grouping of facts 'so that general laws or conclusions may be drawn from them'.

On returning home from the trip, Darwin was very much surprized to receive a letter from Henslow, offering him the position of naturalist companion to Captain FitzRoy, who was preparing a voyage of exploration round the world, on behalf of the Royal Navy. It was overwhelming. Compared with this, a visit to Teneriffe seemed a mere week-end visit, and even the voyages of Humboldt a provincial holiday.

Henslow was most pressing that he should accept. It turned out that the position had been offered to himself, and then to his brother-in-law, the naturalist Jenyns, but owing to their responsibilities they could not accept. There was therefore a serious danger that the wonderful opportunity would be lost to science, and it seemed probable that only a young man would be free enough to go.

Charles at once showed the wonderful invitation to his family, and was quite dashed when they unanimously persuaded him not to go. 'If you can find any man of common-sense who advises you to go', said his father, 'I

will give my consent'. In this atmosphere, Charles forthwith sent a letter declining the offer, and went shooting on
his uncle Josiah Wedgwood's estate. While he was out in
the fields, his uncle sent for him, and offered to drive him
to Shrewsbury to talk things over with his father, for he
had privately formed the opinion that Charles would never
make a clergyman. He thought he ought to accept the offer.
After uncle Josiah had put the case, his father immediately
gave his consent.

Though Charles carried the surname of Darwin, it
should not be forgotten that Erasmus Darwin and the first
Josiah Wedgwood were equally his grandfathers. In fact,
Charles seems intellectually to have been more a Wedgwood than a Darwin, and this may help to explain his cool-
ness towards Erasmus Darwin's ideas, and his lack of
adjustment to his own father. He had the Wedgwood
delicacy, reserve, and critical judgment. It was the second
Josiah Wedgwood who understood him, and enabled him
to accept the *Beagle* offer. Charles used to refer to him
afterwards as 'my First Lord of the Admiralty'.

Charles left the next day for Cambridge to see Henslow,
and then proceed to London to meet FitzRoy. He learned
later that FitzRoy, who was a keen phrenologist, had nearly
turned him down on seeing him, on account of the shape
of his nose.

Captain Robert FitzRoy was only four years older than
Darwin. He was a descendant of Charles II and a nephew
of Castlereagh, a generous, bold, indomitably energetic
officer. He was a high Tory in politics, believing in slavery
on principle, and the literal truth of the first chapters of
Genesis. Through his skill and energy, his expedition returned with charts of no less than eighty-two coast-lines
and eighty harbours. He pressed for a scientific companion
who would 'collect useful information', which would be

of value to a maritime imperial power, and he also thought that accounts of the wonders of nature would celebrate the glory of God, and confute sceptics who questioned any statement in the Bible.

FitzRoy founded the systems of storm-warnings that ultimately led to the establishment of the Meteorological Office. He was subject to fits of passion and melancholy, and in the end, like his uncle Castlereagh, committed suicide.

This was the man with whom young Darwin was invited to share a ship's cabin for several years. That he succeeded is a significant commentary on Charles' personality. The Darwin-Wedgwood Whigs were deeply opposed to slavery, and Darwin had to defend his views, indicating that he did not believe FitzRoy's assertions that slaves were happy.

FitzRoy swore in a violent rage that he could not live with a man who doubted his word. Darwin thought he would have to leave the ship, but presently FitzRoy recovered, and sent his apologies. In those days, it took a good deal of moral courage to oppose a naval captain on any topic on his own ship.

One of the very few recorded instances of Darwin losing his temper was with regard to slavery. His own son William, who had become a banker in Southampton, was dining with him in London during the controversy over Governor Eyre, who had suppressed a rebellion in Jamaica with brutal violence, and had been recalled. Charles had sent a substantial contribution to a fund under the auspices of J. S. Mill and T. H. Huxley, which was being collected to pay the expenses of the legal prosecution of Eyre for murder. Meanwhile, Carlyle, Tennyson, Ruskin and Kingsley were contributing for Eyre's defence.

Feeling was running high, and young William had the nerve to suggest that the Mill fund was being drawn on to finance a banquet. Darwin became very angry and indicated that if that was his opinion, the sooner he got back to pro-Eyre Southampton, the better. After these words, he was unable to sleep at all during the following night, and did not recover his composure until after he had apologized to his son in the morning.

To return to his preparation for the voyage; Darwin secured a stock of simple instruments, reference books, and in particular the first volume of Lyell's *Principles of Geology*, which had just been published. Lyell was another of the wealthy, independent, cultivated Whigs, who had devoted his leisured abilities to working out the new uniformitarian geology, by which past events in the history of the earth were explained in terms of forces that can still be seen in operation. Lyell applied the new theory with consummate ability and expounded the results in an urbane style of the utmost discretion. With Hutton, he found 'in the economy of the world . . . no traces of a beginning, no prospect of an end'. He undermined the position of the creationists, and then protected himself by compromising on the special status of man, who, he contended, was so unique that he could not be included in the rest of the uniform system of nature. Darwin found his geological method incomparably superior at the very first test, when he examined the structure of one of the Cape Verde Islands.

Darwin began his diary of the voyage on his arrival in Devonport, and pursued it thereafter with inflexible determination. He persistently made notes on innumerable aspects, even when he was nearly fainting with utter wretchedness from seasickness.

When he first saw the *Beagle* he was surprized at its small size; it was a brig of only 235 tons, less than 100 feet in length and 25 feet in beam, and yet 70 men were packed into it. His own special corner seemed extremely small, and every cubic inch of the ship had been filled with stores, including more than 5000 cannisters of preserved meat. He soon found the atmosphere of stern naval discipline and intense activity on the ship helpful to the realization of his intentions. He got off to a good start with his own work, and felt an irresistible compulsion to carry on with it through great difficulties of health and circumstances.

He had, however, a very unpleasant introduction to the sea. The *Beagle* was held up at Plymouth by rough weather for about two months before she could finally sail on December 27th 1831. He was laid low by seasickness, to which he ever remained painfully susceptible. Presently the weather improved, and he regained some interest in life. One of the first of his sights was the brilliant snow-capped peak of Teneriffe, disclosed by the clouds against the deep blue sky, a vision which was a 'long-wished-for object' of his ambition. But he was unable to land, owing to an outbreak of cholera in the islands.

He was more fortunate at the Cape Verde Islands, where he had his first experience of collecting in a sub-tropical country. He revelled in the gathering of every kind of specimen, animal, vegetable and mineral, and organized his shipmates as assistants. He delighted in the beauty of the flowers and corals, and as he surveyed the scene and pondered on how it had come to be, the idea of writing a book on the geology of the countries he was to visit occurred to him. It made him 'thrill with delight', but then he suddenly realized the exceeding boldness of aspiring to be an author. Later, when he did produce a book, he said that formerly he could not have imagined that he would ever write one, even if he lived until he was eighty.

As the ship sailed towards South America, new experiences rushed upon him. 'For the first time in my life I saw the sun at noon to the North'. Then he struck the coast of Brazil, and saw the tropical vegetation. Even Humboldt's glorious descriptions with their rare union of poetry and science fell far short of the truth.

The delight that one experiences 'bewilders the mind'. Gaudy butterflies lit on a strange fruit, and crawled over stranger flowers. It was impossible to decide whether all these extraordinary things, or the whole splendour of the scenery, was the more impressive. Delight was a weak word for his 'transports of pleasure' as he wandered by himself in the Brazilian forest. During the day there was an unearthly silence in the shade under the trees, and at night the noise of the insects was so loud that it could be heard on the ship, several hundred yards from the shore. It was all 'nothing more nor less than a view in the Arabian nights, with the advantage of reality'.

It was 'a new and pleasant thing' for him to be conscious that it was his duty as a naturalist to record these things, which at the same time gave him 'so much pleasure'. He noted details of the sea and sky, of plants, animals, people, rocks, birds, clouds, winds, insects, and his mind ranged over them in scientific, aesthetic, and even political reveries.

He heard with joy that the Reform Bill had been passed in England, and having already learned discretion with FitzRoy, wrote home privately: 'Hurrah for the honest Whigs!'

He found an immense deposit of fossil shells and bones in the soft rock of Punta Alta, 'a perfect catacomb for monsters of extinct races'. There was the jawbone of a Megatherium, and huge fossil plates similar to, but much bigger than, those of the living armadillo. He found the tooth of a horse, which much puzzled him, for he had believed that this animal was an importation to South America. He at once noted, and never forgot this tooth, which had belonged to some kind of horse that had existed in an earlier geological age. What was the relation between living horses and those which had disappeared long ago?

They sailed on to Buenos Ayres, where a guard ship had the impudence to fire a warning shot at H.M.S. *Beagle*. In a fury, FitzRoy had a frigate sent to demand an immediate apology, or sink the ship. Charles had a headache from the excitement.

Then they set out for Tierra del Fuego. Charles wrote to Henslow: 'Hurrah for Cape Horn and the Land of Storms'.

In the midst of his industrious labours, he 'almost cried with pleasure' at receiving a letter from his father. 'It was very kind thinking of writing to me'. He sent a message back that it seemed to him that 'doing what little we can to increase the general stock of knowledge is as respectable an object of life as one can in any likelihood pursue'. He still felt in need of self-justification. Then he went on to the glorious prospect of the future, when, after sailing through 'the Straits of Magellan, we have in truth the world before us. Think of the Andes, the luxuriant forest of Guayaquil, the islands of the South Sea, and New South Wales. . . .'

Darwin's perception was raised to its acutest pitch by the romantic excitement of reaching Tierra del Fuego, the land of volcanoes at the very end of the earth, and it was there that nature taught him her profoundest lessons. 'The sight of a naked savage in his native land is an event which can never be forgotten'. The impression sank deep into his consciousness, and when he visited the island a year later, he made many pregnant notes in his diary. What a tremendous difference there was between 'the faculties of a Fuegian savage and a Sir Isaac Newton!' What a scale

of improvement through the range of the human race!
Where could these people have come from? 'Have they
remained in the same state since the creation of the world?'
He wondered what could have tempted men to leave the
fine North, and travel along the Cordilleras, invent and
build canoes, and settle in one of the most inhospitable of
countries. As their numbers seemed not to be decreasing,
they must have become accustomed to the severe conditions.
He supposed that nature had 'fitted the Fuegan to the
climate and productions of his country' by 'making habit
omnipotent'. He had begun to struggle with the problem
of the origin of man.

The *Beagle* sailed through wind and tempest into the
Pacific in June 1834. For weeks together, Darwin was so
ill that he could not write in his diary. The purser Rowlett,
who at thirty-eight had been the oldest man on the ship,
died, and was buried at sea. 'It is an aweful and solemn
sound, that splash of the waters over the body of an old
shipmate'.

In his hammock he pored over the third volume of
Lyell's geology, which had recently reached him, just before making his acquaintance with the Andes. The ship
anchored at Valparaiso. Darwin found the city attractive,
and was even asked by some of its residents for his opinion
on Lyell.

He made an expedition into the Andes, and pondered in
his diary: 'Who can avoid admiring the wonderful force
which has upheaved these mountains, and even more so
the countless ages which it must have required to have
broken through, removed and levelled, whole masses of
them?'

He observed numerous geologically recent beaches on
the sides of the mountains, and concluded that the continent must be steadily rising. Complementary to this rising

movement on land, there must have been a subsiding movement of the ocean bottom. The oceanic islands must be lowered slowly under the waves. When their tops were covered with shallow water, corals would grow, adding layer on layer, so that a coral reef would be formed, whose surface would keep approximately level with that of the ocean, even if the foundation rock under all continued to subside.

He noted the scarcity of animals, and wondered whether it was because none had 'been created since this country was raised from the sea'. Then, at Valdivia, while lying down in a wood to rest himself, the earth began to tremble. He found that he could stand upright, but became giddy. It was like 'skating on very thin ice'. He noted the effect of the earthquake in shattering 'old associations'. He went on to the town of Concepcion, which had been laid in ruins. It was 'the most awful yet interesting spectacle' that he had ever yet beheld.

In places the land had risen two or three feet. On an island thirty miles away, rocks which had been below the water were now ten feet above it. The mighty forces of nature, which, with Lyell, he had seen working in imagination, he now saw in action. Reality conveyed to him a new sense of their power: there were in nature forces capable of achieving virtually anything demanded of them.

The need for a supernatural explanation of even the most extraordinary phenomena was gradually being removed from Darwin's mind.

By this time, Darwin had already been away for more than three years, and was writing nostalgic letters to his relatives at home. 'Snowdon, to my mind, looks much higher and much more beautiful than any peak in the Cordilleras'. He sighed for walks with Whewell and Sedgwick along the Cambridge Backs.

Three years before he had looked with equanimity to the 'distant prospect of a very quiet parsonage'. For those who had the calling, the life of a clergyman was still the 'type of all that is respectable and happy'. But now he was not sure what would become of him. He expected to be home before very long, sitting by the fireside and telling stories of what he had seen. But he looked forward for the moment to the Galapagos islands, 'with more interest than any other part of the voyage'. These are on the Equator, about eight hundred miles from the coast of Ecuador, and with fair winds, the *Beagle* was quickly there.

The first that they struck was a repulsive lava pile, with stunted trees and evil-smelling plants, and looked like 'the cultivated parts of the Infernal regions'.

The next island had a bay swarming with animals, fish, sharks, and turtles. A ship's company caught more than five hundred tortoises in a short time. The lizards were disgusting and the flowers ugly. The birds were 'Strangers to Man', and completely tame. He found tortoises with shells seven feet in circumference, which looked like 'antediluvian animals' or inhabitants of another planet. He moved on to yet another island. This one contained more than two hundred people, political prisoners from Quito, over whom a Mr. Lawson was acting as governor. Mr. Lawson remarked to Darwin that the tortoises from the various islands were all different, and he could tell at a glance from where any one had come.

Darwin did not immediately perceive the significance of this observation. But presently he observed the same phenomenon in the birds, especially the mocking-thrushes. Then he thought again of what Lawson had said. He noted in his diary that it would be 'very interesting to find from future comparison to what district or "centre of creation" the organized beings of this archipelago must be attached'.

It was strange that the islands, so similar in structure, height and climate, could yet be so 'differently tenanted'. He had collected the most suggestive of all his data.

The *Beagle* sailed on to Tahiti, where fine athletic men rowed out in canoes to meet them, but the women were disappointing. FitzRoy noted that either they were not as handsome as they were supposed to be, or his ideas must have been fastidious.

They called officially on the Queen, and FitzRoy apologized for not firing a royal salute, for fear of upsetting his chronometers.

Then they sailed over the vast stretch of water to New Zealand. Darwin was becoming tired and longing more and more for home. As the years went by, he did not become less sensitive to seasickness, but more. FitzRoy became concerned about Darwin's health, and pressed on more and more quickly. New Zealand appeared unattractive. There were few animals, the English were disreputable, and the Maoris treacherous. Among the few things that he liked were vistas of countryside which reminded him of England.

He had set high hopes on New South Wales, but found both the country and the civilization depressing. It seemed to him that Australia had all the social drawbacks without the economic possibilities of the United States. She was 'too great and ambitious for affection, yet not great enough for respect'. He left her shores 'without sorrow or regret'.

Then on to the Keeling Islands, where he found confirmation of his theory of coral reefs, and Mauritius, where he rode on elephants and had an 'idle and dissipated' time. As for South Africa, he never saw a 'less interesting country'. But he found there Sir John Herschel, whose book had helped to form his scientific mind, and enjoyed geological discussions with him.

FitzRoy set the course for St. Helena. Darwin was shocked at the state of the house where Napoleon had been captive, dirty and scribbled over with the names of visitors. He noted that, as on most oceanic islands, there were very few birds and insects.

At Ascension there were no trees at all. He approved of the saying of the wits of St. Helena : ' We know we live on a rock, but the poor people at Ascension live on a cinder'.

Charles found a letter waiting for him at Ascension from one of his sisters, who reported that Sedgwick had told his father that he 'should take a place among the leading scientific men'. He wondered how Sedgwick had formed that opinion, and did not learn until later how Henslow had circulated his scientific letters, and what an impression they had made.

FitzRoy asked Darwin to read portions of his diary to him. He thought that it might be of use to him in writing his report of the voyage. Darwin agreed that he could draw up 'chit-chat' for him, if he thought it was worth publishing.

Instead of sailing straight home, FitzRoy made another run to Brazil, in order to test his chronometers. Though disappointed by the delay, Darwin was glad to have another look at the marvellous vegetation to fix the impression in his mind for ever.

A call at the Azores, and then the *Beagle* sailed for England. Darwin spent the last few days reviewing his experiences. The Tierra del Fuegans left the deepest impression of all. ' One's mind hurries back over past centuries, and then asks, could our progenitors be such as these?'

The map of the world had ceased to be a blank, and had become a 'picture full of the most varied and animated figures'. But as one saw more and more, the 'number of isolated facts soon become uninteresting', and the 'habit of comparison leads to generalization'.

The final run was quick, but the weather very bad. The *Beagle* dropped anchor at Falmouth on October 2nd 1836, after having been away five years. Darwin was almost more dead than alive, owing to seasickness, and he confessed with shame that 'the first sight of the shores of England inspired him with no warmer feelings than if it had been a miserable Portuguese settlement'.

He was pale and weak, but he immediately caught the night mail-coach for Shrewsbury. In spite of his fatigue, his spirits revived, and he controlled his impatience and excitement with difficulty. He even began to wonder how his fellow-passengers could be so stolid at the sight of the beautiful country-side. He now felt that 'the wide world does not contain so happy a prospect as the rich cultivated land of England'.

He arrived in Shrewsbury late on the following night, and instead of disturbing the family household, slept at an inn. On the following morning he walked into his home just before breakfast time, to be greeted with joyous surprize. His father exclaimed that even the shape of his head was quite altered.

He learned that Sedgwick had written to his old head-master, Dr. Butler, that 'if God spares his life he will have a great name among the naturalists of Europe'. Darwin found that his scientific reports of the voyage were being awaited with keen anticipation.

He settled down in bachelor lodgings in London, and at once prepared an abstract of his notes for publication. After he had completed the manuscript, and sent it to the press, he started, in July, 1837, a new notebook, with the heading: *Origin of Species,* in which he jotted down relevant facts and reflections as they occurred to him. He said that he

worked on 'true Baconian principles', collecting facts whole-
sale, without the guidance of any theory. His vast collections of specimens were distributed among the different
experts for study. He was asked to give papers to various
scientific societies, and was persuaded to become one of
the honorary secretaries of the Geological Society. His
manuscript abstract was published in 1839, as his *Journal*.

Darwin described these two years as the busiest of his
life. He even 'went a little into society'. He was astonished
and delighted by the interest and encouragement he received from Lyell, and he used to go to breakfast on Sunday
mornings with Robert Brown. The great Scottish botanist
had observed in 1827 that very small particles in liquids
are in perpetual motion. This phenomenon was used by
Jean Perrin a century later to provide the first direct proof
of the existence of atoms, and was also one of the major
subjects of Einstein's researches.

Darwin's gifts were immediately appreciated by his
seniors. He was elected a fellow of the Royal Society in
1839, at the age of thirty. In spite of all the work and
appreciation, Darwin was uncomfortable in London. His
health was indifferent, and he hated the black, dirty streets.
He pined to rush off into the country, especially to Maer
Hall.

This delightful old Tudor house had been made into an
idyllic oasis by his uncle Josiah and aunt Elizabeth Wedgwood. Josiah created a serious sensible atmosphere, and his
wife a charming one. She was the daughter of an eccen-
tric Welshman who had brought up his daughters to enter-
tain him with good conversation, under the threat of being
horsewhipped. At Maer Elizabeth had the happiness of
exercising her acquirement without the threat. There was
the liveliest interest in every intelligent topic. Visitors could
find good books and papers all about the house, and charm-

ing young men and women with whom one could immediately take up any point.

The grounds of the house had been designed by Capability Brown, with a perfect balance of cultivation and wildness. There was quite a large lake, fed by springs, so that its water was always clear. Boating in summer, skating in winter, fishing, shooting, riding, were available for the intelligent in search of recreation. Charles enjoyed the disciplined abandon of the masses of roses.

Josiah and Elizabeth had nine children, eight of whom lived to enjoy this paradise. Their youngest was Emma, born in 1808, one year before Charles Darwin. She was very charming and attractive, and a practical executive kind of girl, known as 'little Miss Slip-Slop' in the family circle during her childhood, as she did not care for the details of arrangements, as long as the main principles were observed. Like all the family, she was excellently educated. She had a gift for the piano, so, of course, she had received instruction from Chopin.

In the gloom of his London lodgings, Charles meditated on his loneliness. Following his usual habit, he started in 1837 drawing up notes on the pros and cons of marriage, just as he did with regard to the Origin of Species. Among the pros were children (if it pleased God), a constant companion and friend in old age, and the 'charms of music and female chit-chat'. Among the cons were the possibility of a terrible loss of time through a lot of children, and being ' forced to gain one's bread '.

He concluded that it was intolerable to think of spending the whole of one's life ' like a neuter bee, working, working, and nothing after all '. He preferred the picture of ' a nice soft wife on a sofa, with good fire and books and music perhaps', to the dingy reality of Great Marlborough Street. He would 'Marry, marry, marry'.

Charles presently proposed to Emma, and was accepted. Uncle Josiah immediately suggested a settlement of £5000 and an allowance of £400 a year. The spectre of being 'forced to gain one's bread' vanished even more swiftly than it had arisen.

After their marriage in January 1839, the Darwins lived for more than three years in a house in Upper Gower Street. Charles said that he did less work in this period than in any other of the same length in his scientific life. His ill-health became more persistently disturbing. He attended scientific meetings less and less, and gradually withdrew from social intercourse, except with a few friends, such as Lyell. This great man was distinguished by an enthusiastic interest in other people's ideas, and extraordinary openness of mind. When Darwin was young, he had once remarked to Lyell that it would be a good thing if all scientists died at sixty, so that they would be saved from opposing new doctrines. When Lyell in his old age became a convert to Darwin's views, he told him that he hoped he might now be allowed to live.

The Darwins searched for a country house, near London but relatively inaccessible. They chose Down House, near Bromley in Kent. They settled there in 1842, and rarely went away, visiting no one except relatives, and occasionally taking seaside holidays and cures. Darwin never went to France, except for a brief visit to Paris when he was a boy.

Fewer and fewer people were invited to Down, even for dinner parties. The anticipation and lively discussion gave him great pleasure, but this was remorselessly followed by violent shivering and vomiting. He found that the excitement of scientific work enabled him to forget, or it drove away, his usual state of daily discomfort. He devoted the last forty years of his life almost exclusively to the writing of scientific books. He became, in fact, primarily a scientific writer, producing one magnificent book after another, fourteen in all.

In his earlier days he used to think out sentences before writing, but later he found that it saved time 'to scribble in a vile hand' whole pages as quickly as he could, 'contracting half the words', and then correcting them deliberately. 'Sentences thus scribbled down are often better ones than I could have written deliberately'.

He was as methodical as Anthony Trollope in his mode of work. He rose early, and took a turn in the garden before breakfast. Then, at 7.45 a.m., he had breakfast alone. He worked in his study from 8 to 9.30 a.m., counting this period one of his best. Then he went into the drawing room, where his letters were awaiting him. He was glad when there were few; family letters were read to him as he reclined on a sofa. After this, he listened to a novel being read until about 10.30 a.m. He found this a wonderful relief. In course of time, he heard a vast number of novels. He required only that they should have a happy ending, and that the heroine should, if possible, be a pretty girl. He worked again from 10.30 a.m. until about 12.15 p.m., considering that by then he had done sufficient for the day. He went for a stroll, wet or fine, generally accompanied by his dog. He looked in first at the greenhouse, to see how his germinating plants were getting on, and then walked round and round a plot of land about 1½ acres in extent, which was encircled by a gravel path. He had planted various trees beside his path. At one point, he made little piles of flints, and counted his turns by kicking one away each time he completed a round.

When he had had his airing he came in for lunch. He had a passion for sweets, but was forbidden to eat them, though he often failed to obey this instruction. He drank and smoked very little. He went to the drawing room after lunch, and read the newspaper, again reclining on the sofa. It was the only non-scientific literature that he read himself. All other books, novels, travel, history, were read to him. He followed political affairs quite closely.

After he had finished the newspaper, he started answering his letters. He did all his writing in a huge horse-hair chair, with a board resting on the arms to carry his papers. He disliked wasting paper. First drafts were made on bits of envelopes and the backs of old manuscripts. As a consequence, very little of the manuscripts of his great works survived.

He kept all letters sent to him. He had a printed form for answering tiresome correspondents, but was generally too kind-hearted to use it. He sent thanks to donors of books, but not of pamphlets. He distributed many copies of his own books, and expressed surprize at the small percentage of people who thanked him for them. He was delighted with favourable comment, as if he required perpetual reassuring that his work was really worth while.

Promptly at four o'clock he would go out for another half hour's walk. Then from 4.30 to 5.30 p.m., he would work again, even if he had already done a full morning's work. From 5.30 until 6 p.m. he chatted in the drawing room, and then rested again, listening to a novel, and smoking a cigarette.

He gave up late dinner, and had an egg, while the rest of the family were consuming the usual meal. After dinner he played two games of backgammon with his wife, a continuous score being kept for many years. He became very lively over these games. But he could not endure half an hour's serious conversation at night. It prevented him from sleeping, and spoilt his next day's work.

After the game, he read a scientific book for a short

time, and then often lay on the sofa, while Mrs. Darwin played the piano. He generally went to bed at 10.30, and slept badly, being in pain, and suffering from the incessant activity of his mind.

Darwin pursued this routine virtually uninterrupted, for forty years. It enabled him to accomplish a prodigious amount of work. He read extremely widely on every aspect of natural history, including the practical sides, such as gardening and animal breeding. He organized his friends to collect information, and used printed questionnaires which he circulated widely for obtaining facts.

He admired success in business and was keenly interested in his own money affairs, which he kept in almost professional order. He was for thirty years treasurer of the Friendly Club run by the villagers of Downe, and kept their accounts in meticulous order.

From the time of his marriage, he had an income of about £1400 a year, and after 1843, when his father died, his income rose to nearly £5000 a year. He was pleased with the considerable sums earned by the sales of his books.

In the organization of his scientific life, Darwin was as businesslike as a Wedgwood. Indeed, his scientific life was a kind of private enterprize, a most private of private enterprizes. He carried into science the method and outlook of the *laissez faire* manufacturers. Nor must it be supposed that he worked in isolation. He was really the well-to-do director of a large team of voluntary helpers, and toiled at his office, disguised as a country house, digesting and directing their efforts with unremitting attention. It was noted that if he started idling, it was a sure sign that he was really unwell.

Darwin had a brilliant scientific imagination. His mind

seethed with hypotheses. Any interesting fact immediately inspired him to produce a hypothesis. But he found that his first hypotheses very rarely proved to be correct. He relentlessly pursued routine in order to discipline the fertility of his brain and accumulate conclusive proofs.

He wrote that ultimately his mind seemed ' to have become a kind of machine for grinding general laws out of large collections of facts '. His comment on the character of his own mental powers was very similar to Newton's. He attributed his achievement to his power of keeping a problem before his mind with intense persistence for a great many years.

The cause of his forty years of discomfort and pain was never diagnosed. Undoubtedly his brain and nervous organization were highly sensitive. It seems not unlikely that his illness was a form of the nervous indigestion which frequently troubles hard mental workers and writers. It may also, to some extent, have been a psychological protective mechanism. Darwin estimated that the loss of working time from his ' discomfort ' was about equal to that which he would otherwise have ' wasted ' in ordinary social intercourse.

In other directions his health seemed sound. He was the father of no less than ten children over a period of seventeen years. Three of his sons, George, Francis and Horace were elected fellows of the Royal Society, and all were knighted. Sir George Darwin became Plumian professor of astronomy at Cambridge. Jeans and Eddington were his pupils, and Eddington succeeded him. Sir George's son, a grandson of Charles Darwin, is the well-known theoretical physicist, Sir Charles Galton Darwin. Sir Horace Darwin had a leading rôle in founding the Cambridge Scientific Instrument Company.

During the voyage of the *Beagle*, Darwin had been

deeply impressed by similarities between existing South American animals and the fossil remains. He had noted how closely similar animals replaced one another when proceeding southward. He was struck by the South American character of the animals on the Galapagos archipelago, differing from island to island, and yet all the islands were recent and of the same age. It seemed utterly improbable that all of these myriad different yet similar species could each have been individually created. He felt that they could only be explained by supposing that they had sprung from a few original species which had gradually become modified. 'The subject haunted' him.

Though Darwin said that he started collecting facts on the *Origin of Species* without the guidance of any theory, his first notebook on the subject shows that he was in fact grappling with the problem of a scientific law which would explain how these modifications occurred. His mind went out to the law of gravitation. Before Newton, men had thought that each planet was individually kept in its course by God. There was no necessary relation between all of the moving bodies. In 1837, men believed that each individual species of animal was created by God, without necessary relation with any other species.

But would it not be much more simple and sublime to suppose that after the creation of the original animals, all their multifarious successions should arise from them by the operation of some fixed scientific law? This was one of his first ideas, a law which would do for biology what gravitation had done for astronomy.

But what was the law? He tried to think it out, and almost succeeded. He noted that a variety of South American ostrich might have not been 'well adapted, and thus perish', while in a variety with favourable qualities

' many might be produced'. This required the principle
that the permanent variations produced by breeding and
changing circumstances continued, and are adapted to
such circumstances, and the ' death of species is a consequence of non-adaptation to circumstances'.

Darwin had almost worked out the ideas of natural
selection and the survival of the fittest, but they did not
become quite clear to him until the following year, 1838,
when he happened to read Malthus' *Essay on the Principle of Population*. Malthus said that ' Population, when
unchecked, increases in a geometrical ratio. Subsistence
increases only in an arithmetical ratio . . . This implies a
strong and constantly operating check on population from
the difficulty of subsistence . . .'

Darwin saw at once that ' under these circumstances
favourable variations would tend to be preserved and un-
favourable ones to be destroyed. The result of this would
be the formation of a new species. Here then I had a
theory by which to work'.

Malthus had himself got the idea from Benjamin
Franklin, who wrote in 1751: ' there is no bound to the
prolific nature of plants or animals but what is made by
their crowding and interfering with each other's means
of subsistence'.

Darwin was in no hurry to publish his theory. The idea
of biological evolution was far from new. His own grandfather Erasmus, and Lamarck, had put forward versions
of it. The problem was not to conceive the idea, but to
prove it.

He set the machine of his mind and method going, and
for the next twenty years ceaselessly piled up the con-
firmations and conclusive proofs. His accumulation of
material grew larger and larger, and then came a bomb-
shell. In 1858 he received a letter from a young naturalist

in the Malay Archipelago. Alfred Russell Wallace, while tossing with fever in a bed in Ternate in the Moluccas, was thinking about Malthus' theory, when the idea of natural selection as the method of evolution suddenly flashed into his mind. Within a few hours he had thought out the general principles of the theory. His sketch was almost the same as that drawn up by Darwin in his notes nearly twenty years before.

After some anxious moments, the problem of priority was most honourably solved by simultaneous publication of short papers by Darwin and Wallace in 1858.

Darwin's friends pressed him to put his material in order for fuller publication. He had intended to organize it into a huge work, but there was no longer time for this. He made a technical abstract of it all. Then he made an abstract of the abstract. This is his classic: *On the Origin of Species by means of Natural Selection Or the Preservation of Favoured Races in the Struggle for Life.*

Owing to the circumstance of its production, it is the most readable of all the major books on science. It was written in thirteen months, in a uniform and flowing style. Nevertheless, its novelty frightened his publisher, John Murray, who was himself an enthusiastic geologist. Murray found the argument ' as absurd as contemplating the fruitful union of a poker and a rabbit ', and felt that he ought not to print more than 500 copies. He suggested to Darwin that only the section on pigeons should be published and the rest cut out, because ' everybody is interested in pigeons '. Darwin was perturbed by this advice and had an acute attack of ' discomfort ', but humbly refused to budge. An edition of 1250 was printed, and it was sold out on the day of publication.

As an abstract of an abstract, the *Origin* was non-technical, even though very condensed. It could be understood by any intelligent reader who would make an effort, and behind it was Darwin's enormous pile of ascertained and considered facts.

The impact of the book was terrific. By a bit of good work, it was arranged that *The Times* should send it to T. H. Huxley for review. A magnificent notice, three and a half columns long, appeared. (Twelve years later, when Darwin published his *Descent of Man, The Times* review occupied six columns. Those were indeed the days for scientific writers!)

Darwin had shown in a patient modest style that the orthodox theory of the special creation of the animals could not be accepted on rational grounds, and he even made the cautious remark that, by the application of his method 'Much light will be thrown on the origin of man and his history'.

The exponents of the conventional theory of the special creation of living organisms, and man himself, felt that Darwin was accusing God of being an impostor, and claiming to have created things which, in fact, He had not created. Their fury rose, and their spokesmen gathered together at the meeting of the British Association at Oxford in 1860, to do battle for their sacred beliefs.

The Bishop of Oxford, Dr Samuel Wilberforce, had already thundered against the new heresy in the pages of the *Quarterly Review*. 'The principle of natural selection is absolutely incompatible with the word of God.' Evolution was an attempt to dethrone God, and if it was true, 'Genesis is a lie, the whole framework of the book of life falls to pieces, and the revelation of God to man, as we Christians know it, is a delusion and a snare'.

It became known that Wilberforce would attend the meeting, and personally attack the new theory. An excited audience assembled, too large for the assigned lecture room, so it was moved over to a larger hall in the New Museum. Henslow was in the chair, and Huxley came, though he had not intended to be present.

Darwin was not there: the very idea of a public meeting and a speech sent him off into the country with an extra attack of 'discomfort'. His interest in religion had died gradually, long ago. It had not been difficult for his Unitarianism to fade into agnosticism, and he had the well-bred desire to leave the corpse resting in peace.

The audience listened restively to several boring papers. Presently, yet another speaker got up, started by making two marks on the blackboard, and said: 'Let A be the man, and B the maunkey'. The cohorts of prospective young clergymen who had come to support Wilberforce chanted: 'Maunkey, maunkey', and no doubt grinned triumphantly at Huxley, who was on the platform.

Then Wilberforce spoke. He had a plausible, ingratiating style, fluent, forcible, amusing and nasty. He was widely known as 'Soapy Sam', and explained his nickname as arising from the fact that whenever he got into hot water, he always came out clean.

Wilberforce had the majority of the audience with him. He made a characteristic speech, and then ended up with one of his jibes. He turned dramatically to Huxley, and asked him sarcastically whether he claimed his descent from the monkey through his grandfather or his grandmother. We can be sure Huxley's grim mouth tightened. The excitement became almost unbearable. Lady Brewster, wife of the biographer of Newton who had concealed most things about his hero that he did not like, fainted, and had to be carried out. Such was the intensity, that everyone forgot to take any notes. Consequently, there is no official record of what actually happened. According to Huxley's recollection, written a few weeks later, he murmured to his neighbour: 'The Lord hath delivered him into mine hands'.

He rose with dignity, and said that the Right Reverend Prelate had not advanced a single new fact or argument, 'except indeed the question raised as to my personal predilections in the matter of ancestry', but he was quite ready to meet him, even on that ground. 'If the question is put to me whether I would rather have a miserable ape for a grandfather or a man highly endowed by nature and possessing great means and influence and yet who employs those faculties and that influence for the mere purpose of introducing ridicule into a grave scientific discussion—I unhesitatingly affirm my preference for the ape.'

There was uproar. When quiet was restored, Admiral Robert FitzRoy spoke. He contradicted Huxley's facts, and recounted how he had often on the voyage protested to Darwin against his holding views contrary to God's word. He waved a Bible over his head, and asserted the literal truth of every word in it. The chairman ruled him out of order, and he sat down in tragic silence. Four years later, he took his own life.

The debate continued furiously for four hours. When the dust had settled, it was generally felt that Huxley's deportment had been the more gentlemanly, and that the honours of the day must be awarded to him.

Darwin owed much to Huxley's brilliant expository powers. Huxley fought his public battles for him, and described himself as 'Darwin's bull-dog'. There was a remarkable parallel in their early careers. Like Darwin, Huxley at the age of twenty-one also went on a world voyage, as a naturalist on the *Rattlesnake,* and also wrote a diary. It is in striking contrast with Darwin's. He was primarily concerned with the psychological problem of convincing himself that he need not be a failure in life, whereas Darwin had already unconsciously found himself, and was entirely absorbed in science. Huxley mastered his inner feeling of diffidence and became a magnificent public exponent. Darwin's behaviour on the *Beagle* showed that he never really doubted his own scientific powers. He went on working steadily at research, unperturbed, to the end of his life. Being fundamentally confident of himself, he felt no special need to appear in the public arena, and was satisfied with a very retired life.

There was a profound sympathy between the two men, whose greatest powers were complementary. Darwin's genius was primarily creative, that of Huxley, expository. Darwin regarded Huxley as a very clever man who could seize an idea swiftly and express it with extraordinary clarity and force, while Huxley looked to Darwin as the inexhaustibly fertile source of evolutionary ideas and discoveries. Their co-operation was one of the most fortunate events in the history of science.

Darwin established the evolutionary method by using it to explain the origin of species. But he also showed how to use it in many other directions. In his *Descent of Man* he showed how it could be applied in anthropology, and in *The Expression of the Emotions in Man and Animals,* to psychology.

By showing that one species must have arisen from another, he raised the question of how, and thus founded the science of genetics. He explored this science in his *Variation of Animals and Plants under Domestication,* and said that ' a grand and almost untrodden field of inquiry will be opened, on the causes and laws of variation, on correlation, on the effects of use and disuse, on the direct action of external conditions, and so on . . .'

He threw out scores of ideas which have contained

profound truths, even in some of his most criticized conceptions, such as *Pangenesis*. In this he ascribed the
mechanism of heredity to physical entities which he
called gemmules, supposed to be connected with every
part of the body. The modern knowledge of genes and
hormones has confirmed his fundamental idea.

He buttressed his technical position with huge mono-
graphs on barnacles, and important works on coral reefs,
the fertilization of flowers by insects, climbing and movement in plants, crossing, and a big final volume on *The
Formation of Vegetable Mould, through the Action of
Worms*, published in the year before he died.

His range of enquiry was astonishing, and his power of
drawing important conclusions from inconspicuous details
unequalled. Nevertheless, time has, of course, emphasized
many of the obscurities of which he was himself very
much aware. While the fact of evolution became obvious,
its inner mechanism, in spite of all the biological research
of the last hundred years, is still under sharp dispute.

Why did Darwin's work have such an effect, not only
on science, but on the whole of human thought? It was
because it contained principles which were of interest to
many different classes in society.

There were the biologists, who wanted a unified explanation of the multifarious variety of living organisms.
The separate creation of countless millions of distinct
species seemed an utterly arbitrary and incomprehensible
activity. The *laissez faire* capitalists felt that the doctrine
of the 'survival of the fittest', the formulation of the
idea of natural selection which Darwin adopted from
Spencer, completely justified the extremest competition.
They could quote Darwin's assertion that 'from the war
of nature, from famine and death, the most exalted object
of which we are capable of conceiving, namely, the pro-

duction of the higher animals, directly follows. There is grandeur in this view of life . . .'

There were those who felt that God was the symbol of the authority of the ruling classes, by which the general ascent of mankind was being retarded. They found in Darwin's explanation of progress without God a hopeful inspiration, and a release into freedom.

Those who held to the old views, such as Darwin's teacher Adam Sedgwick, were horrified. He denounced natural selection as a 'dish of rank materialism cleverly cooked and served up merely to make us independent of a Creator'.

Much of Darwin's discussion of the social evolution of man led in fact to highly humane conclusions. In his *Descent of Man*, he said that he fully subscribed 'to the judgment of those writers who maintain that of all the differences between man and the lower animals the moral sense or conscience is by far the most important'. As far as he knew, no one had previously considered the question from 'the side of natural history'. After discussing tribal and social life, he concluded that morality and culture were the qualities which led ultimately to survival, and were themselves the product of natural selection. ' Selfish and contentious people will not cohere, and without coherence nothing can be effected'. The extension of co-operation by coalescence of tribes or peoples, and the raising of the moral standard within the society led to survival. He conceived that as man advances in civilization, his sympathies will extend ' to the men of all nations and races'.

The palm did not go to the merely clever: ' the moral faculties are generally and justly esteemed as of higher value than the intellectual powers'.

These aspects of Darwin's teaching were not sufficiently

emphasized by T. H. Huxley, who was inclined to the more dramatic conception of struggle for existence, rather than co-operation for survival.

The extension of the evolutionary conception from biology to other aspects of knowledge has had an enormous influence on modern thought, and has facilitated change and development in every direction.

Darwin's work has, like Newton's, had such immense effect that it seems almost superhuman. This means that it solved not only a fundamental scientific problem, but also gave expression to the intellectual aspirations of the period. Newton and Darwin were symbols of something even greater than themselves. This was the Whig society to which they both belonged, and which ruled England for two centuries. If Newton was an early Whig, Darwin was a late one. These twin stars did not appear in one country by accident: they were comparable manifestations of aspects of its deepest spirit.

Darwin died on April 19th, 1882, at the age of seventy-three. He never received any title. He was buried in Westminster Abbey on April 26th, 1882. Huxley and Wallace were among the pall-bearers, watched by a great array of scientists, diplomats and representative persons. His relations were so numerous that they could not all find places in the procession. Among the general congregation was Thomas Hardy. The poet had come to do homage to the spirit of the age.

REFERENCES

Autobiography of Charles Darwin. Watts: 1929.
Charles Darwin: The Fragmentary Man, by G. West. Routledge: 1937.

MARIE CURIE
1867 - 1934

MADAME CURIE is in the front rank of world scientists. She is the only woman who has achieved this position. Not even the Queen Elizabeth for whom Shakespeare acted occupies such a unique place in history. There have been several great queens, but only one Madame Curie.

That she was a woman adds to her life and work a poignant quality. In the period when she discovered radium, she was an unpaid research worker, looking after a husband whose basic income was £20 a month, and nursing her first baby.

Radium is a very significant discovery. It is the instrument provided by nature to disclose the secrets of the atom, to reveal its structure and evolution, and unlock the fateful sources of atomic energy.

But perhaps it is even more significant that it was discovered by a woman who was at the same time a wife and a mother. And what a family! Her husband was the brilliant physicist Pierre Curie. Her baby grew up to be Irène Joliot-Curie, who shared in the grand discovery of artificial radioactivity.

Madame Curie demonstrated that the greatest scientific achievements are within the scope of women who are both wives and mothers. We naturally ask what has happened to the scientific genius of one half of the human race, from the past to the present, the existence of which has been confirmed by her achievement, but which has hitherto virtually all been lost? Can mankind continue to afford this colossal waste?

It may be argued that little can be done to ensure the discovery and development of such an unaccountable thing as genius. Madame Curie's life does not bear this out. There was nothing magical about her genius. It was distinctly pedestrian, and for that reason, all the more interesting. She had the stubborn acquisitive mind of a Polish peasant woman, whose force had gone into the collection of formulae and observations, instead of copecks and cows. She was a Balzacian character, the implacable protector of the children of her brain, and then the pale unobtrusive widow, who hung on to science even more grimly than death.

Madame Curie was born in Warsaw on November 7th, 1867. Her maiden name was Marya Sklodovska, and both her parents were secondary school teachers. The senior masters in such schools had the title of professor, so her father, who was senior physics master, was known as Professor Sklodovski. Both M. and Mme Sklodovski came from the numerous class of minor Polish land-lord farmers. Their ancestors were not unlike those of Isaac Newton. Many of their relatives had comfortable farms, where the Sklodovski children usually went for holidays. Consequently, it was never necessary for them to go to the cheap holiday resorts usually patronized by the poorer Warsaw middle-class.

Professor Sklodovski's father was the first of his family to leave the land. He studied at St. Petersburgh, and became head of the boys' high school in Lublin. M. Sklodovski followed his father's path. He also studied in St. Petersburgh, proceeding far in mathematics and physics.

Mme Sklodovska was the daughter of a small landowner. She was a very well-educated and extremely beautiful woman. She conducted a private school in Warsaw, for daughters of upper middle-class families.

When she accepted M. Sklodovski's proposal of marriage in 1860, she retained her school, and M. Sklodovski went to live with her in it. Every morning he left the girls' school, to go to the boys' school where he taught physics. Marya Sklodovska was born in her parents' lodgings in the girls' school, the youngest of five children.

The Sklodovskis had now been married eight years. M. Sklodovski was promoted to be professor and under-inspector in another boys' school. His position corresponded to that of senior science master and second master in an English boys' grammar school.

With his new position, M. Sklodovski received an official flat. His wife was finding that the task of conducting her school, in addition to looking after her husband and five children, was becoming too much for her. She could not very well continue to direct it from her new home, and it was no longer financially necessary. Her health was also beginning to fail; she had contracted tuberculosis. The little Marya was for this reason never able to kiss her mother.

As Mme Sklodovska became more of an invalid, sitting in her chair at home, she took up the craft of cobbling. She mastered the cutting out of the leather, and the waxing of the thread. While her husband sat on one side of the stove in the evenings, reposing in his armchair after the day's teaching, she tapped, tapped, tapped the nails into her latest repairs. Mme Sklodovska believed on principle that no useful task was beneath her, and this one was economical, as well as satisfying. Mme Curie at every stage of her career showed the same attitude towards manual work. She undertook laborious physical tasks which were regarded as most unusual among the educated women of Western Europe, and this was one of the habits which enabled her to accomplish a unique achievement.

Marya's three sisters and one brother were known in the family circle as Zosia, Bronya, Hela and Jozio. Her own diminutive was Manya. She was a rather small little girl, with pale grey eyes and fair curly hair, and a very determined mouth. From the beginning, she resolutely held her own end up with her elders.

When she was four, her elder sister Bronya undertook to teach her to read, though she could not yet read properly herself. The two little girls, playing in the garden, made up words out of letters cut in cardboard. Some time afterwards, when Bronya was faltering over a passage in a book which her parents had asked her to read to them, Manya snatched the book out of her hands, and started reading it straight off. There was suddenly an awkward silence. Her parents were astonished, and her sister, three years older than herself, felt humiliated.

This was the first sign of Manya's exceptional intellectual quickness, but her parents, being experienced teachers, were careful not to force her mental development. They coaxed her from reading too much too soon, and encouraged her to play with her dolls and the ordinary infant games.

Manya early showed a strong memory for all the details of her holidays with her country cousins. She was fundamentally a true daughter of the soil.

Meanwhile, M. Sklodovski lived the difficult life of a responsible schoolmaster in Poland, during the days of Tsarist oppression. The head of the school, a Russian named Ivanov, had the task of seeing that the Tsar's policy in education was carried out. As recently as 1863, there had been a determined insurrection, which had held on for eighteen months before it was crushed, the leaders being hung in Warsaw, and many others sent to Siberia. It seemed that open rebellion was not practical, and that the only possible tactic was to concentrate on preserving and extending the understanding of the situation among the Polish youth. A new and thoroughly educated generation might be able to take advantage of a new situation, and, when it arrived, strike a successful blow for freedom. The artists, teachers, scientists and intellectuals in general felt themselves entrusted with a special mission. It was to hold on to their positions at the cost of any humiliation, in order to maintain contact with the youth, and the possibility of secretly instructing them in the sacred struggle for national and cultural independence.

The Tsarist policy insisted on higher education being conducted in the Russian language, with a strict supervision of textbooks and curricula. It became a point of honour in all schools to evade these regulations as much as possible. Insufficient subservience on the part of Polish officials was visited with severe penalties. In 1873, when Manya was six, her father was relieved of his position as second master, his salary was reduced, and his official lodging was taken from him. M. Sklodovski had to find a flat, and take in up to ten of his pupils as boarders, in order to make ends meet.

Mme Sklodovska was sent to Nice in the south of France, in the hope that her tuberculosis might be cured, but she returned in an even worse state. In his desperation, M. Sklodovski speculated with his life's savings of thirty thousand roubles in a brother-in-law's venture, and lost them all.

During the first months of 1876, two of Manya's sisters, Zosia and Bronya, caught typhus. In one room their mother coughed in the last stages of consumption, in another the two girls writhed in fever, and the eldest sister Zosia died.

M. Sklodovski gave his young boarders instruction as well as lodging. Special coaching in Russian was very important, as many children who could work quite well in Polish, did not know the official language well enough to learn in it.

Manya lived in an atmosphere of teaching through the whole of the day and evening. When she was ten years old, she was already two years in front of her age. In her private school class she was first in arithmetic, history, literature, German, French and Scripture. As she spoke Russian perfectly, she was put up by her teachers to answer the embarrassing questions of Tsarist inspectors, engaged in testing whether the education was being conducted sufficiently in Russian.

More signs appeared of Manya's exceptional mental powers. She could recite short poems after reading them only twice, and she exhibited a remarkable power of absorption. She could read a book with complete attention in the midst of a hubbub, with books and chairs flying about. Her early reading was indiscriminate. She read through textbooks and adventure stories, and technical books that she found in her father's library.

Her unfortunate mother died in 1878, before Manya was eleven years old. She had now lost both her mother and her eldest sister. These terrible events proved to be the worst of the Sklodovskis' afflictions. From this period the family's happiness slowly mended. The children grew up into handsome young people. Bronya finished her high-school course by winning a gold medal. So did her brother Joseph, who entered Warsaw University as a medical student.

The three sisters bitterly resented the exclusion of women students from the university. Bronya had become a beautiful young woman, and ardently wished to study medicine.

There was no obvious way, so she began to supervise her father's household.

Manya continued in her high school, working with her characteristic application. It was a tradition among the Polish girls to be opposed to school, as a means of oppression, on principle. But Manya liked learning, and guiltily confessed to her best friend that she really loved school.

She completed her high school course in 1883, before she was sixteen, having won a third gold medal for the Sklodovski family. Her father gave her a year's holiday, to think about her future, and make a calm decision on how she should earn a living.

She spent most of the time with relatives in the country, giving nominal lessons to children, but in fact having a carefree rest in new surroundings and fresh air. She got up at any hour in the morning, from four o'clock to ten o'clock, as she wished. She gathered wild strawberries in the woods. She played battledore and shuttlecock, rolled hoops, went bathing in the river, and fishing for shrimps. She and her girl friends met a charming young actor who picked a large number of gooseberries for them, and was rewarded with a wreath of poppies, pinks and cornflowers, which he immediately wore on his head, and subsequently took back with him to Warsaw.

Her friends had fifty horses, and she learned to be a capable rider. She joined in those Polish winter carnivals, in which young people trailed in sleighs from one big house in the countryside to the next, singing and dancing outside, and receiving lavish refreshment inside. She reported to her bosom friend that it was marvellous, and that she had danced her last dance, a white mazurka, at eight in the morning.

Then she and her sister Hela were invited to stay with

one of her mother's old pupils, who had married a French count. He had an estate at the junction of two rivers, where the girls had a wonderful time. The hosts gave a ball on the fourteenth anniversary of their marriage, and on this wildly exciting occasion, Manya succeeded in wearing out her new russet leather dancing shoes in one night.

After these delightful months, Manya returned to her father's flat. The old schoolmaster had given her a good school education, and an exceptionally cultivated home atmosphere. She had received every reasonable early intellectual advantage. The sad loss of her mother had, however, left her quite undeveloped in the domestic arts. In these she was unskilful, except in sewing.

The idea of giving lessons was always the first thought of a Sklodovski. Manya decided to become a governess. She tramped over the cold and frozen, or hot and dusty, streets of Warsaw to houses where she gave lessons here and there for a pittance, in competition with hundreds of other Polish students as poor as herself.

She was now seventeen, and came in contact with other frustrated young intellectuals. She met a school-mistress aged twenty-six, who was active in political circles. Polish revolutionaries were changing from their romantic literary inspirations of the first half of the nineteenth century to the scientific inspirations of the second half. They were becoming students of Darwin, Spencer and Comte. They aimed at making the new knowledge, which was excluded from the official syllabuses, available to the youth. As it was illegal to teach the higher knowledge without official permission, classes were conducted in secret in what was known as the Floating University. Groups were given courses on biology and sociology in private houses. The system was revived on a large scale in Warsaw during the Nazi occupation in the Second World War.

Bronya and Manya became passionate adherents of this movement. Besides instructing the youth, its members aimed at reducing the illiteracy of the poor. Manya was set to teaching poor women the three R's, and began with the employees in a dress-making establishment.

Commenting on these activities, Madame Curie said that she did not think that the results they obtained were very great, but she believed that their ideas were the only ones which lead to true social progress. She considered that it was not possible to build a better world without improving the individual.

Manya, now nineteen, cut her hair short, and with her sister Bronya adopted a severe but very becoming mode of dress. The two girls had their photographs taken, with expressions of the utmost determination, and sent a print to their teacher-leader with the legend : ' To an ideal positivist—from two positive idealists '.

Besides struggling with the problems of their country, they were also trying to solve their own. Bronya, after winning her gold medal had become in fact her father's housekeeper. She had become a very capable manager and cook, but she aspired to be a medical doctor. This was utterly hopeless in Poland, for the university was closed to women. Manya pondered on her elder sister's difficulty, and conceived the plan of saving enough to help to send her to Paris, where she could graduate. Then she could return to Poland, start practising, and assist her younger sister to follow her to Paris. Manya had first conceived this plan when she was seventeen. Bronya had some savings, and her father could also provide a little. Manya registered at an employment agency for a full-time post as governess.

Her first post was in the house of a wealthy Warsaw lawyer. She was horrified by the vulgarity of their behaviour and conversation, and wrote to one of her cousins that she would not have wished her worst enemy to be in such a hell.

Meanwhile, her sister Bronya had gone to Paris. She had begun to study medicine, and was living in poverty in the Latin quarter. Manya now began to realize more clearly what she had undertaken. Her own conditions of work were very unpleasant, and she was not earning enough to be able to give her sister much help. She looked for a better post in the country, where her own expenses would be virtually nothing. She found one in the family of an estate manager who was a progressive agriculturalist. He farmed beet and ran a sugar factory. When she arrived, she found herself assigned a large and comfortable room. But when she looked out of the window, she was confronted with a chimney which was even smokier than any she had seen in Warsaw. It was the chimney of the beet-sugar factory.

At first things went even better than she had hoped. She found her employers pleasant people. Her task was to educate their ten-year-old daughter, an attractive but rather spoilt child. The engineers at the sugar factory had scientific books and periodicals which could be borrowed. After she had become settled, Manya began to give lessons in the three R's to eighteen peasant children in the village. At nights she pored over books of literature, sociology and science in an unorganized way. Gradually her preference for mathematics and physics formed itself. Madame Curie said later that she did not learn much from these efforts, except the habit of independent work. Among the books that she read at this time was Spencer's *Sociology*.

Then a quite unforseen event occurred. Her employers' student son came home for the holidays, and discovered a beautiful, accomplished and quite strange young woman in the house. She could dance, ride, skate, compose verse and converse intelligently. He fell in love with her. The young man was a little older than Manya, and was agreeable and handsome. She fell in love with him. They seemed well-suited. Marrya had excellent relations with the parents. Both the young people thought there would be no difficulty. But when the young man approached his parents, he found that they were outraged at the idea. How could he dream of marrying a poverty-stricken governess when he was in a position to expect the hand of any well-to-do girl in the region? The young man meant well, but had not the strength to withstand the parental disapproval.

Manya was now in a terrible position: a girl living in the house of an employer whose son had jilted her. She ought to have gone away, but could not. The money for Bronya in Paris was desperately needed, and she had an unconscious hope that somehow she would in the end become engaged to the young man. But she felt extremely miserable, and wrote of saying 'farewell to this base world'. She retired into herself, pursuing her work with a cold determination.

By this time she was down to her last stamp, helping her sister, and now her brother, too. But she worked on. In the autumn of 1888 she wrote to her brother: 'I am learning chemistry from a book'. She had no means for experiments and practical work. Shortly after this she wrote to a friend that her experiences in this country place had been the most cruel in her life, but she had arrived at the 'first principle: never to let one's self be beaten down by persons or by events'.

She had now spent three years in this drudgery. But the Sklodovski fortunes had almost imperceptibly begun to improve. M. Sklodovski had reached the retiring age, and received a small pension. He looked round for some work which would bring in more money, and accepted the very disagreeable post of director of a reformatory. But the salary was good. Bronya no longer needed to call on Manya for money, and asked her father to start putting money on one side to pay her back. From this point, Manya began to accumulate her own little fund which would support her in Paris.

For the Poles, Paris was the symbol of civilization and freedom. They did not wish to go to Petersburgh and Berlin, for those were the capitals associated with the partition of their country.

Her appointment in the countryside came to an end, and she secured another in a Warsaw family of rich industrialists. Her employer was a beautiful and charming woman who ordered her dresses from Worth, but was spoilt by luxury.

Nearly one more year went by, and then, early in 1890, Manya received a letter from her sister in Paris, saying that she was about to marry a Polish friend, and inviting her to come and live with them.

Manya did not at once react to this invitation. She believed that she had already reconciled herself to a broken life and frustrated talents, and she now felt that she ought not to leave her ageing father. She returned to his house and joined again the Floating University. A museum of industry and agriculture had been started as a front behind which science could be taught to Polish youth. It contained few exhibits, but it had a small laboratory. Madame Curie gained her first experimental experiences there, late in the evenings, or on Sundays. She tried to follow the instructions in the practical textbooks, and though she did not have much success at first, her taste for experimental work took root. In handling the test-tubes, balances and electrometers she became aware of her true vocation: she must be an experimental scientist. She inwardly pined for Paris with desperate impatience. Her father wrote that he felt the power with which she aspired to approach that centre of science.

But Manya had not forgotten the young man who had fallen in love with her when she first went into the country. She met him again and found that he was still overawed by difficulties. She told him that if he could not find a way of overcoming them, it was not her business to show him how.

She set out for Paris with a third-class railway ticket, except for the section through Germany, where a fourth-class was available. At last, after six years of waiting and working, she arrived in Paris in the autumn of 1891. Her sister, who was expecting a baby, put her up for the time being.

She went to register as a student at the Sorbonne, and signed her name as 'Marie Sklodovska'. As soon as she began to attend the lectures, she found that both her French and her preliminary knowledge of mathematics and science was painfully inadequate.

Her sister's house was rather a long way from the Sorbonne. It had been chosen as a suitable place for starting a medical practice. Marie, as her official name now was, found that Bronya had married one of the most attractive of the Polish intellectual exiles. He was a medical doctor, and ten years older than her sister. His house was a social centre as well as a surgery. Marie found it pleasant to live but difficult to work there, so, though she had very little money, she looked for a room in the Latin quarter, where she could be free from distractions, and near to her work.

She presently settled in an attic, lit by a skylight, without any amenities. She had to provide her own heating, lighting and water. Like many other poor students of those days, her whole expenditure on rent and living amounted to about three francs, or half-a-crown, a day. She furnished her bare room with an iron folding bed, a small table, a chair, a wash-basin, two plates, one knife, fork, spoon and cup, a kettle and three glasses. She did all her cooking on a tiny methylated spirit stove. She bought her coal from the shop at the corner, and carried it herself up to the attic.

As far as possible, she worked in public libraries, which were lighted and warm, until they closed at ten p.m. For long periods she lived mainly on buttered bread and tea, occasionally eating a couple of eggs in a creamery. She soon lost the healthy look that she had brought from Poland, and began to suffer from fainting. Presently her fellow-students reported her condition to her doctor brother-in-law, who went to see her and insisted on her coming to stay in his house again. After she had been a little restored, she returned to her attic.

With her intense application, she made rapid progress and was given little jobs to do by her professor. She became acquainted with some of the other keen young science students, including Jean Perrin.

She sat for her master's degree in physics in 1893, and came out at the head of the list. The result of these examinations is read publicly in a hall thronged with the excited and anxious competitors. Jammed in the crowd, she was overwhelmed when she heard her name pronounced first.

She tore herself from the circle of congratulating comrades, and rushed off home to Poland for the vacation. Her situation was eased by the award of a Polish scholarship which would support her for more than a year in Paris.

Then she went back, and in 1894 sat for her master's degree in mathematics. In this examination she came second.

Meanwhile, her teacher, Professor Lippmann, had secured for her a little piece of scientific industrial research, consisting in the examination of the magnetic properties of various steels. But no suitable working arrangements were made for her, and she found herself at a loss. At this time she was weighed down with cares, and was writing to her brother on the need for perseverance and self-confidence. Everyone must believe that they are gifted for something, and this thing must be attained, at whatever cost.

It happened that her friend, the Polish physicist Kovalski, was in Paris on his honeymoon, so she asked his advice. Kovalski suggested that she should consult a young physicist called Pierre Curie, who had already done fundamental research on magnetism. Pierre Curie was then thirty-five years old. He had already made discoveries of fundamental importance in other directions, besides magnetism. He and his brother Jacques had made the capital discovery of piezoelectricity. When a crystal of quartz is compressed so that its volume changes, it becomes electrically charged. Conversely, when electrically charged, its volume changes. By submitting it to a rapidly alternating electric current, it can be made to vibrate very quickly.

The phenomenon was subsequently applied by Pierre Curie's pupil Langevin for producing the ultra-sonic waves sent through water to locate submarines.

Already in 1893, before Marie had met Pierre Curie, Lord Kelvin, then the most famous scientist in the world, had written to him about his 'magnificent experimental discovery of piezoelectric quartz'. Kelvin asked when it would be convenient 'to let me come and see you in your laboratory'.

At this time, Pierre Curie had a minor post and a miserably poor laboratory in the Paris Municipal School of Physics and Chemistry. His discoveries had made far more impression in the international scientific world than in his own city. This was partly due to his highly original personality. He was a quiet reflective man of an absolutely uncompromising nature. His inborn characteristics had been heightened by his unconventional childhood. His father was a medical doctor, fiercely interested in politics, and a militant free-thinker. He had not sent Pierre to school but had had him specially and carefully educated at home. This strengthened and developed Pierre's natural tendency for profound original thinking. He graduated at sixteen, and took his master's degree at eighteen. Soon he had made magnificent advances in at least three branches of physics. But his unconventional training had prevented him from learning the habits and traditions of other scientists, and made it extremely difficult for him to fit in with them. He had not grown up in the Normale or the Polytechnique, the two great schools through which nearly all able young French scientists had passed. He did not know their ways, and he had not the support of either of the two schools in obtaining posts. In fact, he had the foible of refusing to apply for jobs, on principle.

Hence, with an international reputation, waited upon by the chief scientist of the age, he had not been promoted above the position of lecturer in practical physics, with a great deal of routine teaching, for all of which he received £12 a month.

Kovalski invited Marie and Pierre to have tea with him in his lodging. She was a novice of twenty-six and he a mature scientist of international reputation, eight years older. The distance between them as scientists was immense.

He was a tall man, who wore heavy loose unfashionable clothes, never raised his voice, and had large steady profound eyes. His mind at once made an impression of power and nobility. He had in his diary written years ago that the scientist pursues an anti-natural path which must necessarily estrange him from women, who are on the side of life and nature, and inevitably try to bring him back to them. He had given up hoping ever to meet a woman who could really understand the soul of science. He was still a bachelor.

Now in Kovalski's room, he found himself deep in scientific discussion with a woman who was not only attractive, but also really understood what he was talking about. He was fascinated by the Polish girl, and sent her a reprint of his famous paper *On Symmetry in Physical Phenomena*. He presently asked permission to visit her, and called on her in her threadbare attic, and it was not long before he proposed to her. But he was at first rejected, for Marie still felt the precedence of her patriotic duty to return home to help her country.

Pierre contended that they were powerless to change the social order, and could do more by some contribution, even if only small, to the advance of definite scientific knowledge. The most important social problems were no longer capable of local solutions, and only general solutions were now possible. To pursue a course which cannot have a successful outcome may cause great harm.

Pierre showed a photograph of Marie to his brother Jacques, who commented: 'She has a very decided look, not to say stubborn'. A whole year passed before Marie accepted him. By that time, Marie's sister Bronya had begun to speak strongly in his favour, and his own mother added her persuasion. They were married on July 26th 1895.

They settled in an uncomfortable flat of three rooms, with the minimum of furniture. In their sitting room was a wooden table, with two chairs. Pierre sat at one end, reading physics, and Marie sat at the other, also reading physics. There was no third chair, in order to discourage callers.

Marie began to study a cookery-book, and made annotations in the margins in her usual style. She found cookery more difficult than chemistry. She continued her measurements of the magnetic properties of steels, and in her spare time prepared to take the examination for a secondary school teachers' diploma. She took the examination in due course, and gained the first place. Her performance as an examinee, working in a language which was not her own, was remarkable. It should not be forgotten, though, that she was several years older than the average candidate.

Pierre's salary had by now been raised to £20 a month, and with her prospect of also being able to earn a teacher's salary, they could look forward to a little more comfort.

Then, in 1897, Marie Curie found that she was going to have a baby. Her father came from Poland to look after her in the country, while Pierre worked on in his laboratory. In the summer vacation he joined his wife, and they decided, in the eighth month of her pregnancy, to go on a cycling tour together. Marie was humiliated to find that she could not keep it up for long, and had to go back to Paris, where, on September 12th 1897, she gave birth to Irène, a future Nobel laureate.

During the next three months, with her babe beneath her eye, she completed her first research, the investigation on the magnetic properties of tempered steels. She began to look round for a subject of research on which she might prepare a thesis for a doctorate.

The period was a propitious one. A new era of science was breaking, and men of insight were prophesying startling events. In 1894 Lord Salisbury had presided over the meeting of the British Association in Oxford, which had not dared to meet there for thirty-four years, after the famous clash between Wilberforce and Huxley. Salisbury took the occasion to review what had happened to the development of the evolutionary idea since that exciting event. He thought that the biologists had not achieved quite as much as they had hoped in their supreme confidence of 1860. He suggested that the next great triumphs of the evolutionary idea would not be in biology, but in chemistry. If we 'turn our eyes to the undiscovered country which still remains to be won', he said, the existence of the several scores of chemical elements was a strange anomaly. The persistent belief in the possibility of the transmutation of other metals into gold suggested that one element could be obtained from another. But the English Conservative statesman and former prime minister found the most significant indications in the periodic table of the elements, discovered by the Russian Professor Mendeleev. His periodic law, he said, strongly suggested that the elements had had a common parentage, and had proceeded through an evolution. 'The dream which lured the alchemists . . . has not yet been refuted'.

At the very same meeting, the discovery of argon, the first of the inert elements, was described. Foremost minds were already preparing to welcome the notion of the evolution of the elements, and the transmutation of atoms.

Then, in 1895, Röntgen discovered X-rays. This gave an intense shock to the whole scientific world. The discovery might have been made at almost any time since the systematic study of electric discharges in evacuated tubes had begun about twenty years before. Several investigators had noticed effects caused by X-rays, without recognizing their significance. But once the rays had been recognized, their startling nature aroused universal attention. Rays which enabled you to see through solid objects were indeed something to talk about and investigate.

Such discussions had occurred in Paris, as in every other

centre of scientific activity. It was typical of the breadth of the discussions that the next great advance arose out of a suggestion from one who was not an experimental scientist at all, but a pure mathematician. X-rays which fell on glass caused it to fluoresce, or shine in the dark. Henri Poincaré suggested that the experimenters should now investigate whether fluorescence of any kind was always accompanied by X-rays. The distinguished mineralogist Henri Becquerel pursued this idea, and examined all of the fluorescent specimens in his fine collection of minerals.

He wrapped up his specimens in black paper, and then laid them in contact with a sensitive photographic plate, and put the whole in darkness in a drawer. If the fluorescent specimens were also producing X-rays, these would go through the black paper and affect the photographic plate. As they were all in dark drawers, daylight could not get in, so no effect could be due to ordinary light.

Becquerel found that in general, none of the fluorescent minerals produced any effect on the photographic plates through the black paper, but with one exception. Materials containing uranium could affect a photographic plate through layers of black paper, and they apparently retained this power undiminished for years.

When Becquerel's discovery was published in 1896, it was widely discussed. Naturally, Pierre and Marie Curie discussed it, for it was interesting in itself, and it had been done by a French scientist in Paris, in a laboratory almost round the corner, so to speak.

When Becquerel made this discovery, its importance was far from clear to himself, or anybody else. It might only be some peculiar form of fluorescence, which is due to light which has been absorbed by a body, and then slowly emitted afterwards.

Marie Curie decided to look into Becquerel's discovery, and see whether it would yield material for her doctoral thesis. It is difficult to say how much of the initiative in coming to this decision was Marie Curie's and how much was Pierre Curie's, but certainly the final responsibility for choosing the subject for her thesis was hers. It was a bold decision, for the phenomenon was quite obscure. It might prove to be of little importance when unravelled, and in that case the candidate's time and labour would have been wasted. Marie Curie took the high line: she did not choose a safe subject which would obviously furnish a sure result after a normal amount of routine work, but plunged right into the unknown. She might very easily have soon returned with nothing more than a disguised old scientific chestnut.

The Polish girl who had prepared for six years to plunge into Paris was prepared to take further plunges, with high confidence and great determination. Pierre Curie sought a working place for her in the School of Physics and Chemistry, but could secure nothing better than a kind of unheated store-room.

There she began to investigate the electrical effects of uranium rays. She used first-class measuring instruments which had been invented by Pierre and Jacques Curie for other purposes. The spontaneity and persistence of the uranium radiation appeared to be a quite unique phenomenon. This was qualitatively important. But within a few weeks, with her good instruments and method, Marie made a quantitative discovery of fundamental importance. She began to give precision to the subject. She proved that the amount of radiation coming from any uranium compound was proportional to the amount of uranium present. It did not depend on the interactions of uranium with other substances, nor on temperature or any other condition, but only on the uranium itself. This meant that the radiation must come from the atoms of uranium: it was an atomic property.

If atoms of uranium have this property, might not atoms of some other substances also have it? She embarked on a thorough examination of materials containing the other known elements, and found that thorium also emitted rays of the same type as those from uranium. Evidently, the property belonged to more than one kind of atom, and might belong to many. She therefore invented the term *radioactivity* to describe the property, wherever it might be found. It was a very happy inspiration.

Having measured how much radiation was produced by uranium, she could deduce the amount of the metal in a piece of uranium ore from the strength of the radiation from the ore.

She started a systematic examination of ores, in order to discover how much uranium they contained. Among these were specimens of the mineral pitchblende. She was astonished to find that this ore was at least four times as radioactive as pure uranium. Evidently it must contain at least one element which was much more radioactive than uranium. But she had examined all the known elements, and had found them all inactive. It seemed, then, that pitchblende contained a hitherto unknown element which was very radioactive.

Professor Lippmann communicated the observation to the Academy of Sciences. On April 12th 1898 a note appeared in the *Proceedings* under the name of Marie Sklodovska Curie, announcing that a new highly radioactive element was probably present in pitchblende.

Pierre Curie now put on one side his own researches and joined Marie in the attack on radioactivity. For his part, as a physicist, he was quite satisfied with the evidence for the existence of the new element. It was known by its physical radiations, which was enough for a physicist.

But the chemists were not satisfied. They would not fully accept the existence of a new element until it, or its compounds, had been prepared in a pure form, and in a tangible quantity. Marie Curie was determined to provide the usual proofs demanded by the chemists, who by tradition were the authorities on the uniqueness and purity of substances.

She set about the task of extracting a chemically identifiable quantity of the new element from pitchblende. It was evident that the amount of it in pitchblende was very small, for the chemists who had many times previously analyzed pitchblende would otherwise have already discovered it. The Curies analyzed pitchblende by ordinary chemical methods into its separate known constituents, and then examined each of the constituents to see whether it was radioactive.

They found that most of them were not active, and that the radioactivity of the whole of the original quantity of pitchblende seemed to be concentrated in two groups of constituents, one with chemical properties resembling those of the metal bismuth, and the other those of the metal barium. By using the property of radioactivity to guide them in their chemical analysis, the Curies became the inventors of the new science of radio-chemistry.

They concluded that there were two unknown radioactive elements in pitchblende, and in July 1898, proposed that the first of these, chemically related to bismuth, should be called *polonium*. So Marie Sklodovska Curie named after her native country the first radioactive element that she discovered.

The Curies were now able to enjoy their summer vacation. They set off on another cycling tour, taking their baby with them, and noting the rate of appearance of her teeth. By the middle of August she had seven, and was able to stand for short intervals.

After the refreshing rest, they were back in their dank laboratory, in full cry after that second new radioactive element. By the end of the autumn they had found sufficient confirmation of its existence, and they published a note in the Academy *Proceedings* for December 26th 1898, stating that they had prepared an extract from pitchblende which was highly radioactive, but which consisted mainly of the inactive element barium. It was evident that the extract contained a new element chemically resembling barium, whose radioactivity must be enormous. They proposed to name this new element *radium*.

This was again a very happy inspiration. It was the perfect name for the new substance, from both the scientific and the general point of view. It described its outstanding scientific property, and appealed to the imagination.

Marie Curie now took the initiative in the immense task of securing a tangible quantity of radium, and thus satisfying the accepted canons of the chemists.

Their work excited intense interest but great reserve. The physicists were shy of new elements with strange properties, which seemed to radiate energy constantly, as if they did not obey the fundamental physical law of the conservation of energy, the very crown of nineteenth century physics. As for the chemists, they almost universally refused to accept statements about the properties of new substances, unless a pure specimen was laid before them.

The Curies had already carried their chemical analysis to the stage which showed that pitchblende must contain less than a millionth part of radium. Hence large quantities of ore would have to be treated in order to secure an appreciable amount of the new element. Radium was chemically associated with barium, and not with uranium. It therefore occurred to them that the waste from the uranium mines should be rich in radium. They applied to the Joachimsthal pitchblende mines for a quantity of waste, and through the influence of Professor Suess, one ton was presented to them. The Curies paid for its transport from Bohemia to Paris out of their income of £20 a month. Then they required a fairly large shed for dealing with the bulky material which looked like peaty coal.

An abandoned shed with a leaky glass roof was assigned to them in the School of Physics and Chemistry. It had previously been used as a dissecting room, but was no longer considered fit even for containing corpses. The Curies set to work on the ton of pitchblende waste. They had no assistance, and had to handle all the heavy material themselves. Owing to the chemical similarity of radium to barium and some other elements, the process of separation was exceedingly tedious. It consisted of separation by crystallization, and involved the solution of mixtures in water, the concentration of the solution by boiling down, and then slow crystallization. These processes had to be repeated thousands of times.

The quantities were not small. They were not operating with test-tubes and glass beakers, but with big cauldrons. Marie Curie spent whole days stirring boiling solutions with an iron rod almost as big as herself. In the evenings she virtually collapsed with physical fatigue.

After the first year she took over the whole of this backbreaking work, and kept it up for a further three years. Pierre meanwhile concentrated on the investigation of the physical properties of the new elements and their products. This could be pursued with delicate electrical apparatus before the substances had been prepared in visible quantities.

Marie Curie handled materials in quantities of about 40 lb. at a time. She carried the containers, poured off liquids and stirred solutions, for many hours together. In wet weather, electrical apparatus had to be taken out of the shed because the rain came through the roof. In cold weather, the high, thinly-built place could not be kept warm. In bright weather, the sunshine was trapped through the glass roof, and the conditions inside the shed became stifling. Yet the Curies found that, in spite of everything, these four years in the miserable shed were the best and happiest of their life.

While Marie Curie with her own hands extracted radium first from one ton of pitchblende, and then from another, and another, until she had dealt with six, the researches on the physical properties of radioactivity were progressing. Other scientists came to work in the same field, and helped in the pioneer work.

At length, by 1902, Marie Curie had prepared about one three-hundredth of an ounce of pure radium chloride, and had determined the atomic weight of radium as 225. She had given the chemists everything they demanded, and there was nothing they could do other than accept the marvellous discovery unreservedly.

Everything about the new element was wonderful. It continuously emitted heat. It poured out extremely intense radiations. It glowed with an unearthly bluish light in the dark.

Marie Curie now considered she had enough material for her doctor's thesis, and proceeded to write it. In the opening paragraph, she described the origin of her researches, and explained that they had led to the foundation of a new method of chemical research, which had enabled her husband and herself to discover radium.

The preparation of a pure radium compound and the

determination of the atomic weight of radium had completed the foundation of the new science of radioactivity, which was now in full evolution.

She then gave a detailed technical account of her researches, followed by a precise summary of her personal contributions, and those made in conjunction with her husband. It concludes with the observation that 'our researches on the new radioactive bodies have given rise to a scientific movement . . .'

With the discovery of radium and the foundation of the new science of radioactivity, which the Curies drew out of Becquerel's original observation on uranium rays, the genius of Marie Curie reached its peak.

Their primary achievement was the establishment of a new branch of science, and the discovery of that terrific and pregnant instrument of nature, radium.

Their researches into the explanation of the nature of radioactivity were fruitful and extensive, but did not touch quite the same heights. Marie Curie wrote in her thesis that 'the cause of this spontaneous radiation remains a mystery, and the phenomenon always presents itself to us as a profound and wonderful enigma'.

'The spontaneously radioactive bodies, and in the first place radium, are sources of energy.' It was not yet known whether the 'energy is created within the radioactive bodies themselves, or whether it is borrowed by them from external sources'.

'We may imagine the evolution of radioactive energy to correspond to a transformation of the nature of the atom . . . accompanied by a loss of weight and by an emission of material particles.'

But she thought that the atom might ultimately obtain its energy somehow from the energy of gravitation, or collect it from unknown radiations passing through space.

Marie Curie's doctor's thesis was one of the greatest in the history of science. She not only received her doctorate, but at the end of the same year, 1903, the Nobel Prize for Physics was awarded jointly to Henri Becquerel and to M. and Mme Curie, for the discovery of radioactivity, of radium, and the foundation of the revolutionary new science.

The Curies' classic work was completed when they were living on Pierre's basic salary of £20 a month, for which he had to give 120 lectures a year, and supervise students' practical work in the laboratory. Marie Curie had her home and her child to look after.

The family had rented a small house with a private garden in the Boulevard Kellerman. Pierre Curie's mother died, and his father came to live with them. Including a domestic help, the household now contained five persons. Pierre took on extra tutoring to meet the increasing expenses. He had applied for a chair in the Sorbonne in 1898, but had been unsuccessful. He was cordially offered a highly-paid chair in the University of Geneva, but the Curies felt he could not accept it because they believed it would have caused a considerable interruption in their radium investigations.

So instead, he got some better-paid extra teaching work, and Marie Curie applied for a teaching post in the ladies' college at Sèvres. This interesting advanced school for girls had been founded by a group of the leading French savants, who themselves gave lectures there. With all of this additional teaching work, the Curies were able to make ends meet.

Then Pierre was persuaded to apply for yet another chair at the Sorbonne. Again he was rejected. His eminent friends insisted on his standing for election to the Academy of Sciences. This involved ceremonial calls, in which the candidate has to explain to existing academicians his own merits, and why he thought he ought to be elected. The antiquated procedure was extremely distasteful to him, and he was not elected.

Then his friends prayed that he would allow them to put his name forward for the Legion of Honour. They told him that the Minister was specially interested in him, and the conferment of the decoration would advance the aim of securing better research facilities for him. He asked his friends to inform the Minister that he did not feel the slightest need of being decorated, but was in the greatest need of a laboratory.

Meanwhile, Marie was labouring away in the decrepit old shed. During the four years she worked there, she steadily lost weight, and in the end, she had lost over fifteen pounds. She began to walk in her sleep. There was a tubercular scar in one of her lungs, but very fortunately the hard life did not cause it to break out again. This was one of the circumstances which made her overestimate her health and strength, and as a consequence, she had an interrupted pregnancy in the late summer of 1903.

Pierre Curie suffered from crippling pains in the legs which were described as rheumatic, but were probably of nervous origin. It seemed as if the Curies would be borne down by their difficulties, but the receipt of the Nobel Prize money early in 1904 eased their material situation for the first time. Pierre Curie still had no chair, no proper laboratory and no personal assistant. One of their first acts with their prize money was to engage an assistant at their own expense.

With the growth of interest in radium, and the discovery that it was of value for the treatment of cancer, the demand for the precious substance increased, and the market price became very high. The Curies received no benefit from this, as they had decided on principle not to patent their processes for its extraction. They considered such action contrary to the spirit of science.

But while they received no financial benefit, and had not yet been given any adequate scientific facilities, they were involved in a large correspondence with scientists all over the world, asking for advice on radioactive research and teaching.

Their first high honour had come from England. Pierre Curie was invited to lecture at the Royal Institution in June, 1903. He was accompanied by Marie, and their friend of ten years' standing, Lord Kelvin, personally supervised the arrangements. He was then eighty-one, and a fabulous figure. Under his influence, the Curies were magnificently entertained. They attended banquets in their plain and somewhat threadbare clothes, and both of them noticed independently and were fascinated by the marvellous diamonds and other jewels worn by many of the guests. During the dinner, Pierre's mind wandered, and he found himself calculating how many scientific laboratories could have been bought with them.

Later in the year, the Royal Society awarded them the Davy medal.

At last, in 1904, a chair was created for Pierre Curie in the Sorbonne, but even then no laboratory was attached to it. In the same year, Marie Curie again found herself pregnant, and on December 6th, her second child, Eve, was born.

Their increasing fame, without a parallel increase in scientific facilities, made their life still more difficult. Their researches were being interrupted by all the calls on them. They felt that they were not making the best use of their time, and were oppressed by a new psychological anxiety.

Their friends and admirers plodded on with the slow task

of securing a proper laboratory for them. The next move was to get Pierre elected a member of the Academy of Sciences. He had already been turned down once, so his objections to standing were more keenly felt than ever. But he was prevailed upon to stand. Finally, in July 1905, he was elected, but only by a narrow majority.

By this time, he was provided with four research rooms, but more important, three posts for co-workers were created. One of these was the position of superintendent of the laboratory work, to which Marie Curie was appointed.

The Curies had left their old shed at the School of Physics and Chemistry with sentimental regrets, but their facilities for research, though not good, were improving. They were able to enjoy their domestic life with less distraction. At the first signs of spring in 1906, they went to their country cottage, taking with them Irène, now eight years old, and Eve, fourteen months. They went for their customary bicycle rides, collected flowers, and rested in their garden. After a few days, they returned to Paris to resume the laboratory work.

On April 19th, 1906, Pierre Curie lunched with his colleagues in the Association of Professors in the Faculty of Science, and after the meal set off to his publishers to see about the correction of proofs. When he got there, he found the office closed, owing to a strike. He turned to walk towards his research rooms. It was a wet day, the pavements were crowded with people, and the narrow street with traffic. Apparently fretted by the delaying crowd, he stepped off the pavement and walked behind a cab, which was clearing a way, as it were, in the traffic. He was probably thinking about some scientific matter, or what he was going to do in his research rooms, quite lost to his surroundings. He presently had to cross the street, and stepped from behind the cab without seeing whether the way was clear. It happened that a very heavy horse-dray loaded with tons of military uniforms was passing by. He collided with one of the horses, which became frightened, and reared. He slipped down on the road. The horses did not tread on him, and he was also missed by the front wheels of the dray. But one of the rear wheels struck his head, and he was killed instantly.

When Marie Curie arrived home that evening from the laboratory, she found her most intimate friends awaiting her in silent sadness. She could not fully understand the dreadful news at first, but when she had finally grasped it, she sank into a cold frenzy. Her profound and powerful nature received a shock in proportion to its own depth. She retired within herself, and no one ever afterwards had access to her innermost feelings.

Hitherto her unexampled scientific labours had been a mighty conquest of the present. She had raised a monument of discovery which had not even been approached by any other woman. Henceforth, she seemed to dedicate herself to the preservation of the past, and the preparation for the future, but was not primarily concerned with her own present efforts.

Madame Curie insisted on the burial of her husband in the Curie family grave. At the Academy of Sciences, Henri Poincaré spoke of Pierre Curie's gentleness and honesty, which concealed a most uncompromising soul, with an ideal of absolute sincerity which was, perhaps, too high for this world.

The authorities discussed what was to be done with the late professor's department, and with its superintendent of research rooms. They decided to appoint Mme Curie to a university lecturership in physics. This was the first time that a woman had been appointed to any position in the French national system of higher education.

Mme Curie's personal life became still more lonely and isolated. She took a small house with a garden at Sceaux, in the suburbs. Old Dr. Eugène Curie, now seventy-nine, and her two little girls formed her family.

She gave much attention to the education of her daughters. Work for their future was one of the few things that mitigated her almost permanent condition of frozen grief. Dr. Curie helped particularly with Irène, a quiet, strong, intellectual, independent character, who had taken so closely after his dead son. A very close affection grew between the radical thinker and admirer of the social movements of 1848, and the future woman scientist who insisted on facing the Nazis, and refused to leave France during the German Occupation.

Mme Curie drew up her own syllabus of instruction for her daughters. She recorded their tendencies and progress in a notebook, and varied the training according to the requirements. The children had to start the day with an hour's work, which might be of an intellectual or manual character. Then they went to the garden and did gymnastics. There were parallel bars, a trapeze, ropes and flying rings. Irène especially became a capable gymnast and sportswoman.

Mme Curie referred to Pierre Curie only with the greatest difficulty when talking to her children. They were not encouraged to indulge in nostalgic reveries, which was in one way good for them, but in another hindered them from developing usual emotional conceptions. As her daughters rarely met anyone except their mother's eminent friends and their children, they did not acquire conventional manners in meeting strangers. For them, everyone was at once on the footing of an intimate acquaintance, to whom the most direct and unvarnished remarks were perfectly natural.

Fortunately, both of them happened to be persons of

great ability. Consequently, their unusual ways became particularly attractive to their admirers. But a combination of high intelligence, natural courage, and unqualified directness could have a devastating effect on various forms of humbug and hypocrisy, and could also, of course, generate terrible rage in philistines.

Mme Curie brought up her family, and consolidated the radioactive science which she had founded. In 1908, the Sorbonne awarded her the title of professor.

Pierre Curie had died at the age of forty-seven, still without a proper laboratory. But radioactivity could not be denied its proper headquarters for ever. It was becoming part of the French national prestige. Slowly the task was accomplished. On a site near the Sorbonne, in a short street to be named 'Rue Pierre Curie', the Institute of Radium was established. One part, under the direction of Mme Curie, was for pure research in the physics and chemistry of radioactivity, and the other was for research on the application of radioactivity to biological problems and the treatment of disease. The two laboratories, though not very large, were handsome, and perfectly equipped according to the ideas of the day.

While these developments were progressing, Mme Curie was engaged in extending radioactive research and teaching. The characteristics of her work since the disaster to her husband had been thoroughness, precise elucidation of details, and exact measurement. Students began to come to her from all parts of the world. She gave them a rigorous training. Her critical judgment was outstanding; very little unsatisfactory work came either from herself or from those working under her direction.

In 1910 she published a comprehensive treatise on *Radioactivity* nearly one thousand pages long. It was encyclopaedic, clear, and exact.

After long years and much difficulty, first the Sorbonne and then the Academy of Sciences had accepted Pierre Curie. After still more years, the Sorbonne had accepted Marie Curie, and then her friends insisted that she, too, should stand for the Academy. If the Sorbonne had been ground private to man, the Academy of Science was absolutely holy. Paris was soon convulsed in a struggle reminiscent almost of the days of Joan of Arc. The battle of men versus women, clericals versus anti-clericals, Frenchmen versus foreigners, right versus left, surged to and fro. The Catholic scientist Branly, after whom the coherer used in wireless telegraphy is named, was the candidate of the opposition, an estimable man, but assuredly not a scientist of the first rank.

When the day of the election came, Mme Curie was defeated by one vote. Men, the Church, France, and Conservatism had been vindicated!

But a few months later in 1911, a second Nobel prize was awarded to Mme Curie, in recognition of her magnificent work on the chemical extraction of radium, and the determination of its atomic weight. She is the only person who has received more than one Nobel prize. In this, too, she is unique.

In the midst of her unexampled achievements and fame, she suffered new miseries. She was a woman, unique and alone, and there were persons in Paris who behaved with a particular kind of viciousness which is seen at its worst in France. Mme Curie was driven almost to the brink of insanity and suicide. But as ever, she mastered herself. 'Whatever happens—one must work just the same'.

The Institute of Radium was completed in 1912, and just as the fine new laboratories were settling into their new rhythm, the First World War began. As the Germans surged towards Paris in their first advance, Mme Curie let it be known that under no circumstances would she leave the city. She considered how she could best serve the country, and it occurred to her that the supply of X-ray field ambulances would be of immense aid to the troops. She found that the army medical services had made virtually no provision for them, so she set about organizing an army X-ray service. She personally solicited ministers, collected equipment from laboratories, and drove a medical lorry with X-ray equipment behind the lines. By the end of the War she had established 220 X-ray units in the French Army, and about one million wounded soldiers received treatment in them.

Like her husband, Mme Curie had refused the offer of a legion of honour decoration for her scientific services. She would have liked to receive the decoration in the military category, but this was never offered to her.

After the First World war Mme Curie became a little more at peace with existence. The intense preoccupations of the war had made the tragic past seem more distant, and she was becoming older. She grew into the figure in which she became most widely known to the world. In appearance she was of medium height. After her husband's death, she generally dressed in black. She was pale and quiet, and was not a ready talker. She had a dry manner of speaking, without artistic sensitivity. She rarely started a conversation, but would always discuss serious science. Her eyes shone when she was interested, and the strength of her personality then became evident. She was unassuming, and quite free from conceit. She was not inclined to be enthusiastic about the work of other scientists. She was a clear but not exciting lecturer, and did everything with a quiet earnestness, as if her work were part of herself. She pursued her relaxations with the same earnestness. She learned to swim very well after she was fifty, and conscientiously joined in the charming diversions of the colony of scientists who used to take their holidays at L'Arcouest on the coast of Brittany. She was fond of reading Kipling and Colette.

After the First World War, she resumed the organization of her institute, her research students, her personal researches, her teaching and her writing. She taught her students that a scientist in his laboratory is not merely a technician, he must learn to see natural phenomena with the wonder of a child hearing a fairy tale.

In this manner she created a school of radioactive research. It is scarcely possible for the complex and varied resources, and the many-sided intellectual atmosphere which are characteristic of a great school of research, to be developed in less than twenty or thirty years. Mme Curie, though she had been by herself since 1906, held on, and brought all this to pass. She had created a great school, and was training fine minds from all parts of the world as well as France, and she continued steadily with her own important investigations.

But it must be said that since 1903, she did not dominate the field as she had done before. Her simple mode of thought, her concrete view, her skill and thoroughness, and above all her incomparable determination, were just what were required at the foundation of the new science of radioactivity. At that time her qualities were supreme, and more important than her husband's. Pierre Curie was much cleverer, but he was inclined to be too subtle. Radioactivity was a quagmire of new phenomena. Someone was wanted who would hold the tiller firmly, and steer the ship of research out safely. Pierre Curie showed signs of faltering, and in this Marie Curie was his superior.

After 1903, different qualities were required for the

supreme leadership of the subject. A critical, hardheaded and realistic appreciation of the facts was no longer the most important requirement. After the basic facts had been recognized, the next task was to explain them. This required a scientific imagination which could conceive how radio-activity might work, combined with the experimental skill which could prove whether or not a plausible conception was true.

Marie Curie had not sufficient theoretical imagination to provide that part herself, and Pierre Curie was inclined to be too speculative. When tragedy overtook them, they had not yet found the perfect combination of theoretical and experimental power for the second stage of the subject. Perhaps they might have found it, but probably not. Another genius appeared whose gifts were exactly suited to this second stage. As Marie Curie had crossed Europe to find her inspiration in Paris, Rutherford had crossed the world to find his in Cambridge. He followed the Curies into the new science, and in 1902 established the explanation of radioactivity as due to the spontaneous disintegration of atoms. Then, in 1911, he proved the nuclear theory of the atom.

But the rich field of radioactive research which Mme Curie had founded in Paris was fertile. A new generation, with a new imagination, grew up in it. Her own daughter Irène mastered her mother's magnificent technique. And then, shortly after the First World War, a young man of fresh genius entered her laboratory. Frédéric Joliot had been a student of the Paris School of Physics and Chemistry, and, like Pierre Curie, did not belong either to the Normale or the Polytechnique. He had been educated by Paul Langevin, who had been Pierre Curie's pupil and successor, and had become the most formative scientist in France. Joliot graduated as an electrical engineer and entered industry, but his heart was in fundamental research. Langevin recommended him to Mme Curie, as a junior assistant.

Mme Curie had prepared everything for the new generation, and within a few years, a galaxy of brilliant results was produced. The fertility of Joliot's ideas and experimental genius, and Irène Curie's critical thoroughness, together with the youthful energy of both, contributed greatly to the discovery of the neutron, and culminated in 1934 in their great discovery of artificial radioactivity— the phenomenon which, as Rutherford told Joliot, he had sought for all his life, but had not found. For this they received the Nobel prize for chemistry in 1935.

Frédéric Joliot and Irène Curie joined themselves in life as well as in science. They were married in 1926.

Mme Curie lived just long enough to see the triumph of her daughter and son-in-law, and the appearance of her first grandchild. She had not only succeeded herself, but had passed the tradition on successfully to the next generation. She probably knew before she died that Irène and Frédéric would receive a Nobel prize.

Mme Curie had worked for nearly the whole of her scientific life with radioactive substances, and for many years before the technique for taking precautions against their effects had been fully worked out. She suffered from radiation burns, and her hands were sore and calloused.

In 1920 she became aware that she was suffering from a double cataract in her eyes. She had operations, and struggled relentlessly against this affliction, devising various special arrangements to assist her sight.

She became pale and more and more anaemic. In the summer of 1934, the disease rapidly worsened, and finally, on July 4th 1934, she died of pernicious anaemia. The cells in the marrow of her spine had gradually been killed by the radioactive radiations to which she had been exposed so long, and were unable to produce the corpuscles which are necessary for the blood. She had been slowly killed by that wonderful radium which she had discovered.

In his tribute to her memory, Einstein wrote: 'It was my good fortune to be linked with Mme Curie through twenty years of sublime and unclouded friendship. I came to admire her human grandeur to an ever growing degree. Her strength, her purity of will, her austerity toward herself, her objectivity, her incorruptible judgment—all these were of a kind seldom found joined in a single individual. She felt herself at every moment to be a servant of society and her profound modesty never left any room for complacency . . . Once she had recognized a certain way as the right one, she pursued it without compromise and with extreme tenacity.'

During her later years, she consented to make formal visits, particularly to Poland, where a great Radium Institute was opened in Warsaw, and to the United States, where she was presented with two grammes of radium for the advancement of research. She was received with virtually royal honours.

She was elected a Vice-President of the League of Nations' International Committee on Intellectual Co-operation, and applied herself to the problems of international scientific bibliography, agreements on scientific symbols, and the preparation of tables of scientific constants. She disliked what she called the anarchy of scientific work, and considered the notion of a scientific general staff for helping to co-ordinate and assist the whole of the scientific activity in Europe.

Besides receiving two Nobel prizes, Mme Curie was awarded eight other major prizes. She was elected an honorary member of eighty-five scientific societies, and received twenty honorary degrees.

According to her wishes, she did not receive any formal funeral, and she was buried beside Pierre Curie, in the family grave at Sceaux.

REFERENCE
Madame Curie, by Eve Curie. Heinemann: 1938.

ALBERT EINSTEIN
1879 - 1955

EINSTEIN was the most famous scientist of the twentieth century. He received an acclaim, among scientists and the public at large, which can be compared only with that which was accorded to Newton and Darwin. This is because his discoveries, like theirs, have been of the highest technical and general significance.

Modern theories of physical nature are of three kinds: classical theory, quantum theory and the theory of relativity. Einstein made major contributions to the first two, and personally created the third. Moreover, he did all this in one year, 1905, when he was twenty-six years old. He was then a patent office clerk in Switzerland, and had not yet met a leading physicist.

Nor was this a transient outburst of genius. By ten years of the most intense and unremitting intellectual toil, from 1905 until 1915, he succeeded in extending his theory of relativity from local physical processes to the movement of the whole universe. It was this latter extension of his theory which most impressed mankind in general.

In addition, he made many particular discoveries, any one of which would have gained for him a place among important physicists. For instance, his proof that mass and energy are equivalent follows as a simple deduction from his relativity theory of 1905. This result is the basis for the precise theory of the release of atomic energy.

Besides his scientific work, Einstein was always concerned

with humane and social questions. His early interest in peace and individual freedom seemed at first to be a reflection of his gentle South German character, and his desire for the best conditions of scientific work. Then his experiences in Germany after the defeat in the First World War, when attempts were made in that country to make the Jews the scapegoat for the disaster, raised his feeling of solidarity with the Jewish community. As the most eminent of living Jews he spoke out with a social courage which was as inflexible as his intellectual determination.

In spite of his intense scientific work and his social efforts, he succeeded in keeping his unique private personality inviolable.

Everyone in the first half of the twentieth century had the inspiration of his presence as a contemporary, whose genius raised the human dignity of the period, and thus increased the spiritual stature of all.

Albert Einstein was born on March 14th, 1879, at Ulm in Würtemberg or Swabia, in South Germany. His parents were of Jewish descent, but his father was a free-thinker, and the family atmosphere was completely irreligious. He was not brought up in the Jewish tradition. The South German background had a strong influence on Einstein's outlook. The people of those parts like a comfortable life, with plenty of fried liver sausage pasties, egg noodles, beer and music. They combine a peaceable disposition with a heavy comic humour, and speak in a thick dialect which is a perfect medium for expressing these characteristics. To the witty aggressive Berliners, the South Germans seem slow-minded country bumpkins.

In that land of unambitious shop-keepers and peasants, Jewish communities flourished virtually in a state of assimilation. Einstein's father, Hermann, was a small business-man. A year after his son Albert was born, he settled in

Munich, and started an electrical business. At first, he lived in a poor part of the town, and there Albert passed his infancy.

Hermann Einstein was an easy-going cheerful man, popular with women and rather casual. He was fond of Schiller and Heine, but was not interested in politics. He liked to take his family on Sunday outings to cafés in the mountains and by the lakes. These expeditions were more popular with the grown-ups than the children, so young cousins were taken along, with whom the children could play. One of these was Elsa, who later became Einstein's second wife. She spoke Swabian and knew how to cook the local dishes, and looked after him most devotedly. Einstein's return to the atmosphere of his childhood showed the strength of its influence on him. He always retained his South German dialect, humour, dreaminess, and tastes.

Hermann Einstein was proud of the absence of Jewish rites in his house, and made anti-religious remarks. These pained his infant son, who had acquired conventional religious feelings from acquaintances. Unfortunately, the little boy could not express himself, as he was very slow in learning to talk. In fact, it was thought that he was sub-normal. He had a governess who called him Peter Langweil, or Master Slow-coach.

Einstein never became good at languages. He lacked skill in pronunciation, and had a weak verbal memory. In his later days in America, his spoken English vocabulary was only about three hundred words.

He became a silent solitary child, with intense religious feelings. Not receiving the traditional religious instruction for which, at that time, he longed, he developed a private worship of nature. The strongest memory of his infancy dated from about the age of five, when his father gave him a magnetic compass. The mystery of its action impressed him. It seemed that something outside the ordinary course of nature was present. He was overcome with a feeling of awe, and could remember that he trembled with wonder at the phenomenon, and turned cold. As he subsequently recognized, it was his first acquaintance with the electro-magnetic field.

His father established a small factory for electrical goods, which were just then becoming fashionable. He did fairly well at the beginning, and the family moved into a larger house with a garden.

Albert was sent to school at the age of six. He had no aptitude for learning by rote, and generally had a miserable time. At the same age, his mother, a lively woman and devoted parent, who liked playing Beethoven, arranged that he should be given lessons on the violin. He received these for six years before he began to enjoy them.

He became a strongly-built boy, but timid and awkward, and consequently preferring to be alone. When he was twelve, he was sent to the Luitpold Gymnasium, a leading high school in Munich. The course was based on thorough drilling in Latin and Greek, enforced by severe discipline. He was very unhappy, and found his school life sheer servitude. Besides his inability to learn languages, he had no interest in physical exercises and sport. These made him dizzy. In later life he suffered from serious heart disease.

He was the only Jewish boy in the school. Nevertheless, he enjoyed the religious instruction given by a teacher whom he liked, until one day this man, who was a Catholic fanatic, produced a nail which, he said, had been used by the Jews in fastening Jesus to the Cross. This affected the attitude of the other boys towards Einstein.

His only pleasant memory of the school was an inspiring teacher of literature, who interested him in Goethe and

Schiller. When he was thirty, and already a professor internationally known in scientific circles, he called at his old school specially to thank this teacher. The man failed to recognize him, and was so surprized at any old pupil visiting him with such a mission that he became suspicious. Einstein got the impression that he thought he had come to borrow money. Both became embarrassed, and Einstein hurried away.

While he benefited little from school instruction, he made progress by himself. An uncle told him of Pythagoras' theorem, and he succeeded in finding one of the easier proofs, by means of similar triangles, by himself. After this, he was given *Euclid* as a textbook at school. He was thrilled by the possibilities of the logical geometrical method. Things which were by no means obvious, such as the intersection of the three perpendiculars in a triangle, were nevertheless capable of rigorous proof.

It seemed to him (erroneously, as he afterwards realized) that scientific discoveries could be made by pure thought, and he pursued the study of mathematics with intense excitement. This was the most beautiful memory of his youth.

He read books on analytical geometry and calculus before he was sixteen, and counted himself fortunate in hitting on authors who gave vivid expositions of the power of these methods, without bothering too much about mathematical rigour.

While he was pursuing these exact studies by himself, he had another piece of good fortune. His family, like many other Jewish families, used to invite a poor student to dine with them once every week, as a social duty. This young man, a Russian Jew, introduced Einstein to the excellent series of *Peoples' Books on Natural Science* by Aaron Bernstein. These gave a descriptive account of the whole of natural science. Einstein read the numerous volumes with breathless attention. One of their effects was to fix his intense but vague religious feelings on to the study of nature. He became profoundly impressed both by its mysteries and its laws, and this experience had a definite influence in forming his permanent attitude towards science, and directing him towards scientific research. He gained from these books also the invaluable acquisition of a general view of science, which was helpful to him for the rest of his life.

When he was about sixteen he pondered on what would happen if one could chase a light-wave at the speed of light. One would keep abreast with the foremost wave, which would appear to be stationary. How then could it be moving, if it appeared not to move?

The paradox contained the germ of the theory of relativity. No doubt many other boys have wondered about the same thing for a while, and then allowed the conundrum to fade from their minds. But from Einstein's mind it never faded. Like the other supreme scientific geniuses, he was able to keep such problems relentlessly before him, until he had forced them to give up their secrets. Unalterable perseverance is one of the qualities of genius. Einstein has repeatedly emphasized that scientific achievement is primarily a matter of character: the will to discovery.

He began to read books on the philosophy of science, such as Buchner's *Force and Matter*, which greatly impressed him. He became a materialist, and more interested in social questions. During his adolescence, however, he received the deepest spiritual experience from the music of Beethoven, Mozart and Bach. He used to improvise private hymns to nature.

When he was fifteen, his father's electrical business began to fail. Hermann Einstein lost his cheerfulness, and the solid family comfort disappeared; he emigrated to Milan to try his fortunes there.

Einstein had never felt deeply attached to his home life. His parents were kind but ordinary middle-class people, who evidently did not have an exceptional understanding for their very exceptional son. Einstein was left behind in Munich, so that his school course should not be interrupted, and was lodged with an old lady. He found the school life more unbearable than ever, and in his isolation concocted a plan for escaping. He persuaded a friendly doctor to certify that he was suffering from nervous exhaustion, and that he should leave the school.

Consequently, he left the Munich gymnasium without having passed the examination which permits entry to the university. He went to his parents at Milan, and was with them for many months before he started school again. He was captivated by Italian life, and found it marvellously free and beautiful after Germany. He abandoned his German citizenship, and did not regard himself as attached to the Jewish community. He wished to be free of all ties, and began to develop what he himself described as his gypsy kind of life.

His father's electrical business in Milan was no more successful than that in Munich. Albert had seriously to think of his future. He was not inclined towards any profession, and had little confidence in his ability to earn a living. As he had shown mathematical ability, and his father was connected with electrical engineering, it was naturally suggested that he should become an electrical engineer. So, at the age of sixteen, Einstein went to Zürich to sit for the entrance examination at the Zürich Polytechnic Academy. He had been away from school for a year, and failed. He had done quite well in mathematics and physics, but badly in everything else. He saw that he would have to remedy his educational deficiencies, so he went to a school in the small town of Aarau, which happened to have very free methods of teaching. Einstein was happy at Aarau. He progressed swiftly, and in a year had secured his certificate for entrance to the university. He made intimate friends, and the son of the teacher with whom he lodged ultimately married his sister.

Einstein now entered the famous Zürich Polytechnic, at the age of seventeen. He studied there for four years, living on one hundred Swiss francs, or about £4 a month subscribed by relatives, as his parents could no longer support him. Lack of sufficient food in this period left him with an impaired digestion.

His main interest at Zürich was in practical physics. He spent much time in the laboratories, fascinated by the direct contact with experimental phenomena. He did not learn much from lectures, but studied the books of Kirchhoff, Helmholtz and Hertz at home. At that time, the mathematics professors at Zürich, Hurwicz and Minkowski, were outstanding. Einstein had a splendid opportunity of learning from them, but he had not yet properly realized the creative value of mathematics in physical research. He was still empirical in outlook, believing that mathematics had only the subordinate function of ordering physical facts. Thus he was unable as a pupil to benefit from Minkowski, who ten years later produced the conception of the space-time continuum, and thus made one of the most brilliant extensions of his former pupil's theory of relativity.

Einstein has attributed his failure to learn from Hurwicz and Minkowski to his deficiency in mathematical instinct. Whereas in physics he always had a good intuition, in mathematics he was not so well able to guess where his best path lay. He subsequently regretted his deficiencies in mathematics, and had to depend much on mathematical collaborators. He could indicate the physical problem to be solved, but needed the help of others in finding the mathematical solution.

As a student he ranged through everything that interested him. He read the philosophers, especially those who had discussed science, such as Hume and Kant. His most profound impression was gained from Hume, who held that the scientific law of cause and effect cannot be based on the phenomena of the external world. Hume strengthened Einstein's scepticism, and helped him to have the courage to question the finality of Newton's principles of physics. Of the moral philosophers, Schopenhauer appealed to him most. He read him in his youth, and his saying that ' a man can do as he will, but not will as he will ', became a guiding idea through all the difficulties of his life.

Many of the young students at Zürich, like Einstein himself, were not Swiss. Among them was a Serbian girl, Mileva Maric, who was also studying physics. They became very friendly, and read physics together. Like most Slav students, Mileva was keenly interested in social affairs, and as a Serbian, in the problems of racial minorities. She was a little older than Einstein. Presently they became engaged.

Einstein began to read Darwin, and other scientific writers fashionable among students interested in social questions.

Another of Einstein's close friends was Friedrich Adler, the son of Victor Adler, the Austrian socialist leader. Friedrich Adler was an idealistic young man, and a conscientious student of physics. He made very thorough and careful lecture notes. Einstein used to borrow these instead of going to the lectures. He spent the whole of his time pursuing his own studies, until a few months before the final examination, when he ' swotted up ' the subjects from Adler's notes.

Einstein and Adler lived in the same house, and Einstein learned from him much about socialist ideas, and also of the philosophical views of the Viennese physicist Ernst Mach. Einstein found Mach's criticisms of Newton's mechanics very stimulating, and from one point of view, the theory of relativity may be regarded as an extension of the revision of Newton's ideas begun by Mach.

When Einstein wrote an obituary notice of Mach in 1916, he clearly expressed his indebtedness to him for the formation of his attitude towards science. ' Nobody who devotes himself to science from other reasons than superficial ones, like ambition, money-making, or the pleasure of intellectual play, can neglect the questions, what are the aims of science, how far are its general results true, what is essential and what based on accidental features of the development? '

Besides borrowing Adler's notes, and benefiting from intellectual discussions with him, Einstein was later indebted to him for another very generous act. Adler had been appointed a lecturer in the Zürich Polytechnic, so he was an obvious candidate for the next vacancy among the assistant professors of physics. When the vacancy arose, Adler insisted on standing down, as he said that the Polytechnic could not afford to miss the opportunity of securing a man of Einstein's talents.

In 1915, in the early period of the First World War, Friedrich Adler formed the opinion that a possibility of peace was being obstructed by Stürgkh, the Austrian prime minister, whom he regarded as being responsible for the war. He went into a restaurant where the prime minister was dining, and shot him dead. Adler was duly condemned to execution. He spent his last hours correcting a paper which he conceived to be a refutation of Einstein's theory of relativity. An unsuccessful attempt was made to get him reprieved, on the ground that his article against the universally accepted theory showed that he was out of his mind.

Einstein's tendency to anarchic isolation grew in this intense life of the poor foreign students. He aimed at emancipation from all ties, conventional, racial and religious. He became as detached from his Jewish as from all the other elements in his background.

He neglected his clothes and personal appearance, and developed those unconventional traits which marked him out from so many other men. He discovered that it was not necessary to wear socks or pyjamas, and thereby economized in darning and washing. He abolished as far as possible the wearing of collars, and a leather boating jacket became one of his favourite articles of attire. It was loose and very comfortable and never wore out. When he became director of the Prussian Academy of Sciences' Institute of Theoretical Physics, he used to lecture in a sports shirt, flannel trousers, and tennis shoes.

He took his Zürich examination in the autumn of 1900, and did very well. He gained a diploma of university standard, which gave him the possibility of qualifying as a teacher.

The intense grind for the final examination at Zürich produced in Einstein a strong temporary distaste for science; about a year passed by before he could focus his mind on scientific work again with pleasure.

He made very severe criticisms of methods of university instruction and said that it is nothing short of a miracle that they 'have not yet entirely strangled the holy curiosity of inquiry'. This is a ' delicate little plant' which, apart from stimulation requires mainly freedom. He considered it a very grave mistake to suppose that ' the enjoyment of seeing and searching ' can be pushed forward by ' coercion and a sense of duty '. He commented that even a beast of prey would lose its appetite if forcibly fed under a whip.

Einstein's abilities as a student had been noticed, and suggestions had been made that he might be appointed to the staff of the Polytechnic. But after he had graduated, no appointment materialized. It appeared that one of the senior lecturers disliked him and had raised objections against him, so he looked for any job that he could find. As he was not a Swiss citizen, he could not get a good teaching post, so he started the formalities for obtaining Swiss citizenship, and became a temporary teacher in a provincial technical school. The uninstructed young artizans were mostly older than himself, and at first ' pulled the leg ' of the naïve young man, but presently they were fascinated by his explanations of science. Without realizing their own change in attitude, they began to listen to him with rapt attention.

When his job came to an end, Einstein was engaged by a coach to tutor two backward children. He found this an interesting task, and enjoyed solving the problems of how to present knowledge in the easiest possible way, and had such success that his employer became jealous and dismissed him.

Once more he was out of a job and scarcely knew where to turn. He was helped by Marcel Grossmann, a mathematician and an old fellow-student at Zürich. Grossmann persuaded his own father to give him a letter of introduction to Haller, the director of the Swiss Patent Office at Berne. Haller was a remarkable character, a fierce democrat according to the principles of 1848, who paid no man any more respect than he considered that he deserved. Being very able and competent, the authorities put up with him.

When Einstein called on Haller, he expected that the

director would at most give him a few minutes' interview. It had not occurred to him that at this preliminary stage it would be worth while learning any details of patent work. He was therefore quite abashed when the rugged old man at once put him at a desk in a corner, and submitted him without notice to a two hours' examination. He gave him various patent specifications, and asked him to give his opinions on them. Einstein knew nothing of the kind and method of formulation of opinion which would be required, and Haller, of course, observed his complete ignorance of these things. He said, however, that his comments had been intelligent , and he would give him a job.

His Swiss naturalization papers came through, and he was appointed one of twelve clerks who dealt with engineering specifications. He began work at the Swiss Patent Office in the autumn of 1902. He was very happy in this post. He had a modest but permanent salary, and the work was not heavy. The office had an eight-hour day, and he found he could get through an official day's work in three or four hours. He devoted the rest of the office hours to his private researches, working on bits of paper, which he hid in a drawer when anyone came into the room. Thus the theory of relativity and his other early prodigies were produced, in a manner similar to that in which Jane Austen wrote *Pride and Prejudice.*

Early in 1903, a few months after he had secured his patent office clerkship, he married Mileva Maric. They secured a top-floor flat in an apartment house, and were deliriously happy. Their first son was born in 1904, and Einstein was now indeed a man inspired. He thought out in these months three of his masterpieces, which were published in his miraculous year of 1905.

He secreted deeper and deeper thoughts in the drawers of his room in the unsuspecting patent office, and at home was sent out to wheel the baby in the pram, dashing back to his flat from time to time as some new thought occurred to him. One thinks of Newton dashing up the stairs from his garden at Trinity, to note a new idea. But Newton did not suffer the handicap, nor enjoy the inspiration, of an infant.

Einstein was always particularly attached to the circumstances of his life in the Swiss Patent Office. It seemed to him that there was a great deal to be said for modest posts which gave a scientist enough to live on, but left him free from teaching and administrative responsibilities, and did not draw upon his creative intellectual abilities. He often recommended such 'shoemaker's jobs' to scientists.

When he left Germany in 1933 after the rise of the Nazis, he addressed a great public meeting in the Albert Hall in London, under the presidency of Lord Rutherford, in support of action for the protection of science and learning. It was the first time that he had spoken in public in England, and the vast audience waited with intense expectation to hear him. After some remarks on the dependence of scientific discovery on freedom, he said that an idea had occurred to him recently, to which he would like to give expression. The thousands who had come to hear the greatest of living intellectuals leant forward in tense anticipation. He described how he had lived in solitude in the country, and how he had found that the monotony of a quiet life stimulated the creative mind. Would it not be possible to find places for scientists in various isolated occupations which do not make much demand on bodily and mental effort? He thought of such posts as those in lighthouses and lightships. Could they not be given to young scientists, so that they could concentrate on problems undisturbed, during the most productive period of their lives?

A rustle ran through the deep silence as hundreds of listeners turned to their neighbours and remarked that if scientists were put into lighthouses they would probably forget to turn the lights on, with disastrous results! Hitherto they had listened to Einstein with awe; now they listened to him with affection. It was evident that he was a man of the most direct and simple personality. Few of the listening thousands knew that he was speaking from his own early experience at Berne. It was characteristic of him to recognize things as they are quite directly, and follow the consequences wherever they might lead, and however unusual they might be.

Before he had graduated, Einstein wrote a paper in which he attacked Boltzmann's theory of gases. His professor refused to sponsor it for publication, out of deference to Boltzmann, who was then the most eminent theoretical physicist in Central Europe. By 1904 Einstein had already published five papers, mainly on the theory of heat, but they did not foreshadow the explosion of 1905. Undoubtedly his first marriage seemed to have put a crown on his life.

Since the age of sixteen he had pondered on the speed of light, and had wondered what the world would look like if one could travel through it with that speed. He had learned sceptical courage from Hume, and the obscurities in Newtonian mechanics from Mach. He mastered the recent work in theoretical physics. A major part of this was concerned with the meaning of the fundamental discovery by Michelson in 1881, that the speed of light is constant, whether or not its source is moving.

According to the old ideas of space and time, this seemed absolutely incomprehensible. Surely the speed at which light travels must depend on the speed of its source. If a lamp is moving swiftly along a straight line, it would be natural to suppose that the rays of light travelling forward from it in the same direction would receive, in addition to their ordinary speed, an extra speed due to that of the source. Yet experiment proves decisively that this is not so.

The leading physicists of the day tried to escape from the paradox by inventing special hypotheses, or mathematical tricks, which would enable one to describe the experimental results without making any change in the fundamental conceptions of physics. It was an unsatisfactory patching-up process, but the senior theorists could not do better than this, because they could not escape from the presuppositions of a lifetime. A young fresh mind of the necessary power, without many commitments in the world of ideas, was required to look at the situation afresh. As Einstein himself said, ' the theory of relativity arose out of efforts to improve, with reference to logical economy, the foundations of physics as it existed at the turn of the century'.

The essence of the theory is that space and time can be understood only in terms of moving bodies, and the real things we know. Absolute space and absolute time, conceived as separate from matter, are fictions which do not exist. Instead of trying to find ingenious scientific subterfuges, Einstein considered the central fact of the constancy of the speed of light, and tried to think out what it implied. He discovered that the idea of the simultaneity of two events has a limited significance, and that two events which appear simultaneous to one observer may not appear simultaneous to another observer.

He worked out the implication of this discovery in the intensest excitement, in five weeks. When he had finished the paper, he was prostrate for a fortnight in a condition of nervous reaction and shock. It is only thirty pages long, and the title describes it as dealing with the electrodynamics of moving bodies. Unlike most scientific papers, it has no list of references at the end, for it was the beginning of the new subject of relativity.

Thus Einstein read the riddle of the constancy of the speed of light, and explained what it implied. In 1944 a manuscript copy of his 1905 paper was auctioned at a Kansas City war-bond rally for six million dollars, and deposited at the U.S. Library of Congress.

Einstein had had to break away from Newton's definitions of space and time, which had scarcely been questioned for two hundred years, and had been the basis of prodigiously successful advances in science. It should be understood, of course, that Newton's conceptions are not wrong. They are true within the earlier range of experience, and will always be true so long as the bounds of that experience are not exceeded. Einstein subsequently showed that Newtonian conceptions are a particular case of a wider range of ideas required to explain facts discovered long after his period.

The other great paradox of the age, reaching even deeper than the constancy of the speed of light, was Planck's discovery in 1900 that an accurate description of the way in which energy is radiated from hot bodies can be given only on the assumption that it is emitted in units, or quanta, of finite size. Hitherto energy had been conceived as continuous. When a hot body cools down, it seems to radiate heat energy in a continuously decreasing manner. Planck himself was dubious about the meaning of his idea. It certainly solved problems, but he was inclined to regard it as a mathematical trick which would presently be explained away in terms of the old physical conceptions.

The free and unattached young patent clerk in Berne took a much more radical attitude. He supposed that energy really was emitted in discrete units, or quanta, and looked around to see whether the idea would help to explain any unsolved problems in nature.

For more than a hundred years, physicists had been thoroughly satisfied that light was transmitted by a wave motion. The wave theory of light had explained beautifully and perfectly a multitude of most refined and exact experiments in optics. Then, near the end of the nineteenth century, the photo-electric effect was discovered. It is the phenomenon upon which modern television depends. When zinc and certain other metals are illuminated by a beam of light, it is found that electrons may jump out of them. But this does not happen unless the light consists of waves of less than a certain length.

Furthermore, if electrons do jump out, they all have the same energy, or speed, like a volley of bullets from a machine-gun. Thus a beam of light, if its waves are short enough, acts like a kind of trigger which causes a volley of electrons to jump out of the metal. If the beam is made more intense, the speed of the emitted electrons does not increase, but there are more of them.

These phenomena are quite inexplicable by any wave-theory. Einstein showed, however, that they could be very simply explained if a beam of light consisted of discrete units, which he called *photons*. These are, as it were, atoms of light.

He showed that the energy of these photons was simply connected with the wavelength of the light, by means of Planck's idea of the quantum. His extremely bold conception and very neat calculation were published in a paper which contained only sixteen pages.

It was for his quantum theory of light, *not* for his theory of relativity, that he was awarded a Nobel prize in 1921.

Nor was this by any means the end of the wonders of 1905. Einstein had been deeply impressed by Mach's criticisms of physical ideas, and was indeed much indebted to them. But Mach's criticisms sometimes went too far. He had dwelt upon the inconclusive character of the evidence for the existence of individual atoms. Davy and Faraday, for instance, had never once made any use of the idea of atoms in their great contributions to science. The chemists only handled billions of billions of atoms at a time.

Thus the idea of an individual atom might seem to be no more than a useful hypothesis. Mach went further, and denounced individual atoms as fictions. Einstein saw the force of Mach's objections to the atomic theory, and agreed that the evidence for it was defective. But he felt that Mach had been carried away by his own arguments, and had exaggerated their weight. Einstein's sense of physical reality told him that atoms existed, even if the existing arguments for them were defective.

So he set about finding a conclusive proof that atoms really exist. If a fluid consisted of atoms, bumping each other in a random way, each atom would follow a zig-zag path, according to the laws of chance. If the fluid contained particles much larger than atoms, they also would be bumped about by the atoms, but their motions would be smaller because they were heavier. Einstein calculated the size of the motions of those larger particles, and arrived at the surprising result that particles of one five-thousandth of an inch in diameter, though enormously heavier than individual atoms, nevertheless would show a slight but perpetual zig-zag motion, sufficiently large to be seen under a microscope. He published this result, not knowing that Robert Brown, Darwin's friend, had actually observed such motions, seventy-eight years before.

Einstein's calculation showed how the size and mass of individual atoms could be calculated from the Brownian motions of small particles suspended in fluids, and Perrin duly carried out the appropriate experiments. Thus, also in 1905, Einstein gave the conclusive theoretical proof of the existence of atoms, according to the ideas of ancient Greek philosophy and Newtonian physics.

But even this does not conclude his labours of 1905. He also carried on the mundane task of publishing the thesis for his doctorate. For this he did not reserve one of the classics of science, but only a first-rate paper on a new method of calculating the size of molecules.

The importance of Einstein's papers was immediately recognized by the greatest minds. Max Planck wrote to him at Berne in 1905, congratulating him on his theory of relativity. The Polish physicist Witkowski read his relativity paper and exclaimed to his colleagues: ' A new Copernicus has been born '. Perhaps Einstein may be more truly compared with Copernicus than with Newton, for he was exclusively concerned with ideas and theories, whereas Newton was also a great experimental scientist, and a great innovator in mathematics.

In the years before 1905, Einstein hammered out his mighty ideas in discussions with a few intimate friends and fellow-students, with his wife Mileva, the young engineer Besso, the Rumanian student Solovini, and a mathematician called Habicht. He was not in contact with any senior scientist.

After 1905, the more far-seeing men at Zürich desired that he should be appointed a professor. But he had no academic position, and no lecturing experience. It was arranged that he should lecture at Berne University, while still working in the Patent Office, so that he could later be promoted to Zürich without administrative difficulties. Only two students came to his Berne lectures, one of whom was his friend Besso. He did not present his subject-matter in any formal manner, but just said what he thought about it. A senior Zürich professor attended one of his lectures to assess his quality as a lecturer, and was not pleased. He told Einstein afterwards that if he wished to be appointed to Zürich this manner of lecturing would never do. Einstein replied quite sincerely that he would not mind at all if he was not appointed to Zürich, for he was really very happy at the Patent Office.

In 1908, Einstein was invited to speak at an international congress at Salzburg. This was the first time that he met leading scientists as colleagues. Then, in 1909, he was invited to be assistant professor at the Zürich Polytechnic. The change did not bring any increase in salary, but it gave him a place in the academic world, and converted him into a research worker by profession. In order to eke out their income, the Einstein family took in lodgers.

All of his investigations up to this time had been done from pure love of research into the phenomena of nature, more in the spirit of an artistic amateur than a professional investigator. He conceived the typical investigator as a ' singular, taciturn, lonely fellow ', which was of course, a description of himself. He was entirely absorbed in following out his own profound ideas, and was not much interested in others, except in so far as their knowledge and interest could be of aid in solving his problems. He was not a good professor in the ordinary sense, making his pupils competent in knowledge which would be useful to them. There were gaps in his knowledge of elementary physics which were unbecoming in a professor. He sighed for the Patent Office, and freedom from routine academic duties.

At Zürich, his second son, Eduard, was born. As a professor, he began to meet the leaders of physics. In 1909 he became acquainted with the great Dutch physicist, H. A. Lorentz, whom he came to esteem more than all his other contemporaries. Lorentz was much older than Einstein, and had taken the conventional ideas as far as they would go. He was a man of the finest character, quite without ambition, but with extraordinary abilities which naturally made him the leader in any scientific gathering. Besides having a magnificent command of physics, he was kind and modest, and a splendid linguist. He was generally voted into the chair, and helped discussions forward with exquisite skill.

Einstein, the spiritual orphan of genius, found in Lorentz a kind of intellectual father, who could hold his hand in the academic world, which was so much tougher than it looked.

Einstein was appointed a visiting professor at Lorentz's university, Leiden, in 1912, and remained a member of the faculty in this capacity for sixteen years. He was becoming known personally, as well as by his work. He now had two children, and a growing reputation, and he found it difficult to live on his assistant professor's salary. In 1911 he was offered a full professorship in the German university in Prague, and felt he could not reject the much higher salary. At that time there were two universities in Prague, the ancient Charles University, the oldest university in Central Europe, and the German University, which was a modern outpost of German influence in a Slav country. Einstein found the atmosphere more like that of a political organization than a university. He detached himself entirely from the dominant political preoccupations, and buried himself in his thoughts.

He went for long walks in the beautiful streets of Prague, and pondered on his theory of relativity. In its first form, he had worked it out for bodies moving in straight lines. He wanted to extend it to bodies moving in curves under gravitational forces, so that he could apply it to the description of the movements of the planets and stars. ' The general theory of relativity,' he said, ' owes its origin to the attempt to explain a fact known since Galileo's and Newton's time but hitherto eluding all theoretical interpretation: the inertia and the weight of a body, in themselves two entirely distinct things, are measured by one and the same constant, the mass . . .'

Thus Einstein's great extension of his relativity theory, like his foundation of the theory itself, arose from his power of thinking out the implications of a simple and thoroughly well-known fact. ' Science,' he said, ' is no more than the purification of daily thoughts.' During his Prague walks, he thought out the new physical conceptions which were required for this general theory of relativity. He found that they could not be expressed in ordinary mathematics, and began a long struggle to find the appropriate kind of mathematics, and learn it.

During these days of absorption in Prague, Einstein's life was restricted to the German community. He could not speak Czech, and he was very deeply involved in his researches. He was able to detach himself from the acute problem of relations between Germans and Czechs, and felt himself to be an alien Swiss. Mileva Maric could not ignore the passionate struggles of her fellow Slavs for national independence. Einstein and his wife began to drift apart.

After being in Prague for a year and a half, he was invited to return to Zürich as a full professor. He was glad to return, and continued his struggle to work out the general theory of relativity with intense energy. He got much mathematical help from his old fellow-student and friend, Marcel Grossmann.

He had not been back at Zürich very long before an eminent position became vacant in Berlin. As part of the general policy of promoting German greatness, the Kaiser Wilhelm Society had been founded in order to advance science under the most splendid conditions. Professorships with high salaries and the most agreeable conditions were created to attract the greatest scientists in the world. One of these chairs had been occupied by the Dutch chemist van't Hoff, who died in 1913. Owing to the determined efforts of Planck and Nernst, Einstein was invited to succeed van't Hoff. Planck and Nernst travelled to Zürich to persuade him to accept the invitation. All professors in Germany were, however, members of the Civil Service, and as such, German citizens. Einstein did not like Berlin, but the offer was of a kind which could not very well be refused. He made his acceptance of the invitation conditional on his being allowed to retain his Swiss citizenship, besides being formally a German as a civil servant. This proved later to be very important, for it saved him from the more extreme persecution from which Galileo had suffered. His condition was accepted, and he arrived in Berlin early in 1914.

The breach between Einstein and his wife had widened. His family did not accompany him to Berlin, but remained in Switzerland. His first marriage was dissolved shortly afterwards, and he married his widowed cousin Elsa, who had been his playmate in his South German childhood.

He was in the midst of his creation of the general theory of relativity, and had scarcely settled down in Berlin when the First World War shook the world like an earthquake.

All the intense German life, political, military and intellectual, seemed to explode in August, 1914. Einstein watched with bewilderment, and without any feeling of contact whatever, the frenzied crowds marching up and down Unter den Linden. He wrote to Romain Rolland that friends who hitherto had seemed to think clearly, were now struck blind by the intoxication of patriotism. He refused to sign the notorious manifesto of ninety-three leading German intellectuals, accusing the countries which had been attacked of being engaged in a conspiracy against a peaceful Germany, on the ground that he was a Swiss neutral. But he courageously joined the pacifists G. Nicolai and W. Förster in their appeal to the intellectuals of Europe to work for peace.

He was not molested, but he was treated as a moral leper by most of his colleagues. When he attended meetings of the Prussian Academy of Sciences, the chairs on each side of him were left ostentatiously empty. He wrote in March 1915 that even scientists in various countries were behaving as if 'they had had their brains amputated'.

In spite of all the stress, he worked on at his general relativity theory, and in the autumn of 1915 he got it out. He had discovered that gravitation could be brought within the scope of relativity theory with the aid of the mathematical theories of Riemann, and he had found that his equations described the movements of the planets even more accurately than Newton's.

It had been known for a century that the planet Mercury has a small aberration which cannot be explained by Newtonian theory. It revolves round the sun in an ellipse, but each year the ellipse is slightly displaced. In fact, the ellipse itself makes a complete revolution once in about three million years.

Einstein wrote to Sommerfeld on November 28th, 1915, describing his discovery. 'Now the marvellous thing which I experienced was the fact that not only did Newton's theory result as first approximation but also the perihelion motion of Mercury (43″ per century) as second approximation. For the deflection of light by the sun twice the former amount resulted.'

This is truly one of the most wonderful paragraphs in all science, and is the final proof of the immensity of Einstein's genius. His wonderful year of 1905 was not some strange freak of nature, but was followed by ten years of sustained effort at the same height of intellectual intensity, culminating in further results of equal importance, and even more spectacular nature.

It is very striking that while Newton worked out his theory of the universe in the midst of the Whig rebellion, Einstein worked out his in the midst of the First World War. Evidently, the kind of distractions which deter scientists of supreme genius are not of the kind which one might expect, nor does it seem likely that it is mere coincidence that the creation of the two great modern theories of the universe should have occurred in the midst of wars.

Einstein knew well the magnitude of his own discoveries, and he was always modest about them. He repeatedly said that Maxwell's contributions to physics were greater than his own, and that Faraday and Maxwell's conception of the electromagnetic field is the profoundest idea in science.

As for Newton, ' this brilliant genius . . . determined the course of western thought, research and practice to an extent that nobody before or since his time can touch . . .' Newton not only succeeded in expressing the laws of motion as differential equations, but invented the differential calculus for that purpose; an achievement which is 'perhaps the greatest advance in thought that a single individual was ever privileged to make '.

Only history can decide what place Einstein himself will finally occupy in this hierarchy of genius, but assuredly it will be very high.

Einstein published his new results in 1916. It was obvious that the next step was to see whether his forecast of the amount by which light rays would be bent by the mass of the sun was correct. This could be done by observing stars very close to the sun during an eclipse. The light from the star would be bent as it passed by the sun, and the amount of the bending could be calculated by measuring how much the star appeared to be displaced from its usual position in the sky.

Germany was, however, at war and surrounded. Her astronomers could not send expeditions to suitable places outside the country, where an eclipse could be seen. Now the Dutch astronomer de Sitter received copies of Einstein's papers. He sent one of these to the Royal Astronomical Society in London. The Secretary of the Society happened to be A. S. Eddington, who received the paper in his official capacity. Eddington was a Quaker, and one of the few scientists in England not involved in the First World War. Besides having the time to study the paper, he was also one of the few men in England, perhaps the only one, equipped to understand it. There is a story that a friend remarked to Eddington that there were only three people in the world who understood the theory of relativity. Eddington looked troubled, and his friend told him that he need not feel too modest. 'Oh, no,' Eddington replied, ' I was trying to think who the third might be.'

In spite of the war, and the interruption of international scientific co-operation, Eddington devoted his great astronomical abilities to the leadership of two expeditions, one to South America and the other to Africa, to observe the solar eclipse of 1919. Besides this professional work, he explained the new theory to the general public in popular books of unsurpassed brilliance.

When the English eclipse expeditions reported that Einstein's prediction of the amount of the bending of light rays by the sun had been triumphantly confirmed, a furore broke out. The public was intrigued with the idea of ' space caught bending '.

In Berlin beaten and bitter Germans were looking for someone to blame for their misfortunes. Here was this Jew who had refused to fight, and had spent the war loosening the foundations of the universe. Many of them felt in a confused way that he had helped to undermine Germany. Some German scientists made furious attacks on the new theory in public debates held in theatres, and Einstein himself attended one or two of these sitting in a box, and giggling in high-pitched laughter at the more ludicrous mistakes.

While the general relativity theory was being denounced in Berlin as a new Jewish corruption, French scientists in Paris were fulminating against it as the latest attempt at world-domination by German science.

Until the end of the First World War, Einstein had not felt himself particularly attached to his Jewish background, though he had described his religion as Israelite when he went to Prague in 1911. He never learned Hebrew, and when he later visited Jerusalem, he lectured in French. But in the face of increasing anti-Semitism he felt it his duty to stand by his own people.

In 1919 he attended a conference in Berlin organized by Zionists to discover the problems and the future of the Jews. Without subscribing to the Zionist principles, he demonstrated his solidarity with the Jewish people, and in spite of his habitual detachment gave all practical help within his power. Einstein commented on the odd contrast between his passionate sense of social justice and social responsibility, and his pronounced freedom from the need for direct contact with other human beings and human communities. He deeply desired the well-being of other people, without wishing to know them personally.

He said that his experiences in Berlin especially with non-Jews made him fully conscious, for the first time, of his Jewish background. He was also shocked by the attitude of prosperous Berlin Jews, who looked down on the numerous Jewish refugees from Eastern Europe. Many of these came to Einstein for help and advice, and he was touched by their admirable and pathetic belief in the value of science and learning, so much more pure than that of the clever people in Berlin who despised these humble refugees. He gave away the whole of his Nobel prize money, helping various causes.

Einstein was offered the Presidency of Israel, but felt himself unfitted for the position. He assisted Weizmann and introduced him to Rathenau, in whom he had confidence. After Rathenau was murdered, Einstein's wife arranged for her husband to be shadowed by bodyguards. He spent three months out of Germany at Leiden, and then went on a grand tour of China, Japan, Israel and Spain. When he returned, Germany was in the midst of the inflation which destroyed the old social structure of the country.

The immediate cause of the disorder was the demand of the Allies for impossible reparations, which created a situation that was skilfully exploited by reactionary elements in Germany. Einstein considered that this had arisen through a lack of the most elementary international understanding, and it heightened his interest in the League of Nations' International Committee of Intellectual Cooperation, which he had been invited to join in 1922. At its first meeting, he made a vehement speech in favour of the organization of scientists in an international body, and he denounced the majorities of scientists in all countries, who had forsaken their international obligations at the first breath of war.

When the French occupied the Ruhr, he resigned from the Committee, on the ground that, as a convinced pacifist, he could no longer have any relations with a League which had not the power to prevent such a deplorable event.

Then he discovered that the occurrences in the Ruhr were not so simple as he had supposed, and he wrote to the Committee that he had been badly advised, and would in future be glad to help it, though he had resigned. He was, of course, invited to re-join, and Bergson as chairman ' welcomed M. Einstein, both as a new and as an old member '. The Committee established the Institute of Intellectual Co-operation in Paris. Mme Curie was a member, and these two extraordinarily detached personalities took to each other at once. They performed curiously reversed rôles. Einstein made emotional speeches and dramatic exits and entries. He exercised the prerogative of a *prima donna,* while Mme Curie backed him up with masculine administrative persistence.

After its meetings, the members of the Institute used to dine at a fashionable restaurant. On one occasion, the violinist in the orchestra happened to play one of Einstein's favourite melodies. Einstein was soon lost in reverie and wandered from his seat to the orchestra, and borrowing the violinist's instrument, began to play the piece. Everyone listened in curious and respectful silence. But as time went on, a certain embarrassment arose. Diners were getting hungrier, and waiters awkwardly did their best on tip-toes. After an hour or so, a new band arrived to play the late night dance music, and an increasing number of young couples waited impatiently to dance. In the end, someone plucked up courage to tell Einstein that the hour was late, and that it was time to leave.

Einstein was often quite unconscious of his public impression. Infeld has told how they once went to a cinema in Princeton together, to see a film of the *Life of Emile Zola.* They bought their tickets, which were collected as they went into a crowded waiting room. There were still fifteen minutes to wait before the film came on, so Einstein suggested they should go for a stroll in the fresh air. When they went out, Einstein became suddenly concerned that they had no tickets, and asked the doorman innocently: ' Will you recognize us? ' The doorman thought he was joking, and said : ' Yes, Professor Einstein, I will '.

In Berlin, Einstein lived in a typically middle-class flat; apart from a grand piano there was nothing unusual in the furnishing. When he had married for the second time, his wife had brought him two step-daughters. A happy relationship grew up among the new family. His wife Elsa was entirely devoted to him and her two children. She was very short-sighted but did not like to wear spectacles, and Einstein was always helping and guiding her movements. With his ideal of absolute independence, Einstein never became completely intimate with anyone, but he liked to see others happy and smiling. He would make puns and jokes to this end. In him there was something of one of Shakespeare's sublime clowns. He laughed loudly, and had an obvious joy of living.

Music was one of the needs of his life. He played the violin proficiently and enjoyed being accompanied on the piano, and playing in trios and quartets. When he was by himself he improvised on the piano compositions which resembled Mozart. He interrupted scientific calculations to play on his piano, as a kind of restoration of his equilibrium after mental effort.

He was quite ready to perform at charity concerts, and was proud of having collected 6000 dollars at one organized for the relief of victims of Nazi persecution. Sometimes he consented to appear with a young violinist in order to help him with publicity. At one of these concerts, the musical critics had been invited to hear the young musician, and a critic who did not know that Einstein was a physicist wrote in his paper that Einstein's playing was excellent, but that he did not deserve his world fame, for there were many other violinists at least as good.

Einstein did not lose interest in other people's work after his own prodigious successes. In 1924, Langevin gave him an enthusiastic account of Louis de Broglie's doctoral thesis, in which he invented the modern wave-theory of matter. De Broglie's theory was the counterpart of Einstein's own theory of light-waves as particles. Einstein delivered a report on the new theory to the Prussian Academy of Sciences, and his immediate support secured for it a quick acceptance. At the same time, he adopted and developed the theory of the Indian physicist Bose, on the statistics of particles which cannot be distinguished from each other.

His chief outdoor recreation was sailing. In his earlier years in Berlin he used to sail with a doctor friend on a yacht. Then he took to sailing a little dinghy on the numerous lakes of the river Havel, in the Berlin environs. He was very skilful at manipulating his boat, and he enjoyed the gliding motion and the distant prospects of the not too clear shores and landscapes, which soothe the mind. He could be seen almost every day in his old sailing clothes, with his big body and rippling muscles. Sailing also had the advantage that it gave him fresh air without heavy exercise, which he could not support owing to a delicate heart.

As the date of his fiftieth birthday approached in 1929, the municipality conceived the plan of giving its most distinguished citizen a commemorative present. It learned that he had no place of his own where he could moor his boat, which he used to leave at a place belonging to one of his friends. The municipality decided to present him with a house beside the lakes, which would give him perfect quiet, and direct access to the water. They had acquired an estate which contained just such a house. The decision to present the house to Einstein was published, and then it was discovered that though the house had been acquired by them, its occupant had reserved the right to live in it during his life-time. The municipality then decided to build a new summer home for Einstein in the grounds, and this project was published. Then it was discovered that the occupant of the old house also had the right to object to the erection of any new house on the estate during his occupation.

The affair became a matter of municipal politics. Members of the council who later became Nazis were determined to make everything as difficult as possible. The council officials made yet a third attempt to find a solution. No site near the most attractive part of the Havel was available, so they found another further from the city. But it turned out that there was no approach to it, except through private grounds. For the third time, the Berlin municipality had bungled the arrangement, and there were loud public laughter, cartoons and comic articles on the ridiculous inefficiency of the governing body, not of some isolated country village, but of one of the greatest and most modern cities of the world.

A municipal deputation called on Einstein to discuss how the painful affair might be solved. By this time, all pleasure in the thought of the birthday present had evaporated. They suggested that he should find a site which would suit him, which they would then purchase and build a house on it to his own design. A suitable site was found at Caputh, a village by the lakes near Potsdam. Plans for a house were made, and the project was submitted to the Berlin Municipal Council for final approval. The Nazis moved that it should be referred back, and gained their point. Einstein announced that under no circumstances could he accept the gift. He wrote to the mayor that while the decisions of magistrates seemed to take a very long time, human life was short, and he could not wait any longer for the realization of their kind intentions. He finally decided to buy the land at Caputh himself and build the house at his own expense.

So, at the end of 1929, he had a delightful country house by the lakes, and some of his personal friends presented him with a new solid mahogany dinghy.

He meditated in his boat on the final aim of his scientific life, the discovery of one unifying theory which would bring together the hitherto separate phenomena of gravitation and the electromagnetic field. He advanced numerous ideas on this subject during the last quarter-of-a-century, with his characteristic concentration and obstinacy. Unlike his earlier major efforts, they have not commanded general acceptance.

Pondering on the quiet waters at Caputh, the rising turmoil in Germany did not seem as near to Einstein as it actually was. He noted the social phenomena, and expressed his disgust. He wrote in 1930 how he abhorred the military system. ' That a man can take pleasure in marching in formation to the strains of a band is enough to make me despise him. He has only been given his big brain by mistake; a backbone was all he needed. . . . Heroism by order, senseless violence and all the pestilent nonsense that goes by the name of patriotism—how I hate them! War seems to me a mean, contemptible thing: I would rather be hacked in pieces than take part in such an abominable business.'

On all possible occasions, he expressed his belief in absolute pacifism, and his admiration of men such as Gandhi. He was particularly fond of Hume's view:

' When I observe two nations engaged in war, I seem to see two drunkards fighting with cudgels in a china shop. Not only will it take them a long time to heal the scars which they inflict on each other, but they will have to pay for all the damage which they cause '.

Einstein had no use for political manoeuvres, and believed in the ultimate superiority of forthright speech: ' I am firmly convinced that the passionate will for justice and truth has done more to improve man's condition than calculated political shrewdness which in the long run only breeds general distrust '. He denounced the ' type of conciliatory attitude which is a crime against humanity ', and those who ' are trying to pretend that it is political wisdom '.

He was very energetic in encouraging the pacifist movement. He calculated that if only two per cent of conscripts refused to fight, all armies would be disorganized, and war would become impossible.

He had no illusions about his lack of direct influence. People flattered him, he said, as long as he did not embarrass them. But as soon as he made pointed suggestions, they resorted to insults and calumny.

As the power of the Nazis increased, it was evident that his life in Germany was no longer safe. But it was difficult to get him away from the apparent peace of Caputh. The local villagers, and especially the children, were very friendly. Einstein had been invited to Christ Church at Oxford in 1932, but he did not feel at all at ease in the close-knit stylized English upper-class social life. He longed to get back to Caputh, in spite of the Nazis.

He accepted an invitation to lecture at the California Institute of Technology. On his way through New York, he was taken to see a Protestant church with bas-reliefs of famous scientists. The parson proudly showed Einstein his effigy, and Einstein remarked that he might have imagined that a Jewish saint could have been made out of him, but he had never expected that he would become a Protestant one.

Einstein returned again to Berlin, where the atmosphere was still more tense. He was burdened with new personal troubles, for he began to receive incoherent letters from his younger son, who was in Switzerland. The young man, who was sensitive and delicate, had idealized his father and had cultivated the same tastes of science and music. No doubt he had not the mental and physical strength to be able to follow his father's path in any satisfying degree. His affection turned to hatred, and he became mentally ill. Einstein went to see him in Zürich, and on his return never fully regained his former happy humour.

His elder son studied agricultural science, and ultimately became a professor of hydraulics in California.

In the spring of 1932, Einstein was invited to join the Institute for Advanced Studies, which had recently been founded by Abraham Flexner at Princeton in the United States, on behalf of a wealthy American donor. He accepted the offer provisionally and went to Belgium for a scientific congress, but still longed to be back sailing at Caputh. While his friends were trying to persuade him to hurry off to America, he glided over the quiet waters with even greater absorption than before.

Meanwhile, the American League of Patriotic Women petitioned the American Government that Einstein should not be allowed to enter the United States, as 'a communist and a menace to American institutions'.

'Never yet,' wrote Einstein, 'have I experienced from the fair sex such an energetic rejection of all advances; or if I have, never from so many at once.'

Einstein departed from Antwerp for America in December 1932. Paul Langevin went to see him before he sailed, to secure his consent to stand for a chair at the Collège de France in Paris.

He was in California when the Nazis actually seized power. It surprised him, for he had underestimated their political ability. He heard that his home in Berlin had not yet been violated, and his bank account was intact. He left for Europe again, and while at sea heard of the first systematic actions against the Jews. When he landed at Antwerp on the return, he decided to stay in Belgium. He was personally friendly with the King and Queen, whom he had met through the Solvay scientific congresses in Brussels.

Once, when he had arrived in Brussels and found himself without money, he went into a pub in a poor district and asked in thick French whether they had a telephone. They told him there was one in the bar. Then he asked how to ring up the Royal Palace. The publican and his customers listened in astonishment to an awkward dialogue coming from the open door of the telephone box, in which the strange man was asking laboriously to be put through to the Queen. The word went round that he was a lunatic or an anarchist. A crowd assembled round the pub, and when Einstein came out of the box after his lengthy efforts, he found two policemen at the door waiting for an ambulance to take him to an asylum. This was one of the rare occasions when he was not recognized.

Now, on the later occasion, he thought at first that he would have no difficulty in living *incognito* in Belgium.

He published a declaration that as long as he had any choice he would stay only 'in a country where political liberty, tolerance, equality of all citizens before the law are the rule', and he hoped that 'Germany will soon recover her sanity and that in future men like Kant and Goethe will not only be remembered from time to time, but that the principles they taught will prevail in public life and in the conscience of the people '. He sent in his resignation to the Prussian Academy of Sciences.

His wife and step-daughters were in Berlin. Their bank account was confiscated, and it was high time for them to leave. Large numbers of Jews still did not fully understand the danger, and many blamed Einstein for his plain speaking, saying that he had provoked the Nazis. Commenting on this later, Einstein wrote that ' Anti-Semites often talk of the malice and the cunning of the Jews, but has there ever been in history a more striking example of collective stupidity than the blindness of the German Jews? ' Just as many Berlin Jews did not welcome the East European Jews after the First World War, so now many French Jews did not welcome the German Jewish refugees in Paris. ' Jewish solidarity,' said Einstein, ' is another invention of their enemies.'

The French Minister of Education, de Monzie, now offered Einstein a vacant chair in the Collège de France. It was the chair for German studies, and it turned out that de Monzie had not secured the assent of the governing body of the Collège de France before making the offer. The Collège refused to confirm it. The Einsteins left for Princeton in the autumn of 1933.

In the new land Einstein was in a way more isolated than ever. ' I live in that solitude which is painful in youth, but delicious in the years of maturity,' he wrote.

His wife had always been delicate, but it was now found that she had a serious disease. She worked hard at making a new home for her husband in America, but presently she was driven to her bed in a fatal illness. She died in 1936. Einstein tended her with sympathetic understanding, and was much occupied in trying to make her last days as happy as possible. But even this distraction characteristically did not interrupt his scientific work, which continued with the usual intensity. After the death of his wife, his life became still more impersonal and lonely.

Abraham Flexner's idea in founding the Institute of Advanced Study was to create in the United States a centre of the highest intellectual quality. His studies of American universities had led him to conclude that in spite of the vast material developments, and the excellent work done in some places, America had not yet discovered the secret of quality in intellectual work. He believed that even when good work was done, its effects were dulled by the much greater quantity of lower grade work in the same places. He therefore aimed at an institution which severely restricted itself to work of the highest class. There is no recipe for the creation of such institutions. They usually grow out of a complex of circumstances too subtle for analysis. But one way of helping to start them, though very far from infallible, is to recruit a small staff of the highest talents.

Flexner was fortunate in securing Einstein's acceptance, as his presence, more than that of any other scientist, instantly conferred on his institute an atmosphere of distinction. The strongest of all intellectual stimulations is the presence of genius. The young man of talent can learn from personal contact what real genius is like, and gain the inspiring idea of what is humanly possible.

Einstein's presence was by far the most important of his contributions to Princeton. He was accessible to qualified persons, but he was, as ever, interested only in his own line of research. He gave lectures only when he felt like it, or had some new result to publish. He had the most perfect conditions for undisturbed work, though he was fond of saying that he was not dependent on conditions, and could work anywhere.

He worked on and on at his attempts to discover a unitary theory of gravitation and electromagnetism, with only occasional personal collaborators. Few physicists were interested in his undeviating search for a new comprehensive theory of all physical nature, and most were concerned with advancing the new quantum theory, with which he was out of sympathy. His divergence on this subject became pronounced after 1927, when Heisenberg published his Uncertainty Principle, according to which atomic phenomena cannot be known with absolute precision, but only to degrees of probability. With regard to this, Einstein said: ' Some physicists, among them myself, cannot believe that we must abandon, actually and forever, the idea of direct representation of physical reality in space and time; or that we must accept the view that events in nature are analogous to a game of chance'.

Though Einstein had been the boldest of the developers of the original quantum theory, he refused to follow the still more radical new quantum theory. He believed that the probability theory of matter was a reflection of human ignorance, and that ultimately the startling ideas of the new quantum mechanics would be explained by a deeper understanding of the older, more conventional ideas.

As he put it, he believed in the fundamental reasonableness of nature. He once expressed his belief in the words: ' Raffiniert ist der Herr Gott, aber boshaft ist Er nicht'—in English: 'God is subtle but He is not malicious', or in American: ' God is slick, but He ain't mean'.

His departure from conventionality made him in America even less influential in administrative matters than he had been before. He gave favourable testimonials to almost anyone, as long as he was convinced that the recipient was not a crook. On one occasion he gave testimonials to each of four scientists applying for the same job. When it was pointed out that by giving testimonials to more than one candidate he had destroyed the influence of all of his testimonials, he replied that in each case he had stressed a different quality, and it was for the appointees to choose the one they preferred.

As the horrors of persecutions in Nazi Germany multiplied, Einstein's absolute pacifism was shaken. He was presently forced to the conclusion that it was necessary ' even to face battle ' in order to ' safeguard law and human dignity '.

The discovery of the phenomenon of uranium fission, with its promise of the large-scale release of atomic energy, by Hahn and Strassman, in Germany at the end of 1938, raised this question in the acutest form. The addition of atomic weapons to the Nazi armoury was a possibility of the most appalling significance. At the beginning of 1939 the vast majority of native Americans did not feel this threat. The atomic bomb was a dream, Europe was far away, America was very powerful, and no one would dare to attack her; if Europeans wished to fight among themselves, then leave them to it. The gifted Jewish scientists who had found refuge in America had a far more realistic sense of the danger. Following on Hahn's discovery, scientists in several countries demonstrated that a chain reaction of uranium fissions, which would produce atomic explosions of enormous power, was probably possible.

Led especially by L. Szilard, several of the most eminent of the refugee scientists tried to persuade the American authorities to investigate the possibility with all speed, in order that the Nazis, at any rate, should not make the atomic bomb first.

Official American opinion, like that of general American opinion, was not inclined to believe that the Nazi military threat, or the atomic bomb, was imminent. The only way of circumventing this complacency seemed to be a direct appeal to President Roosevelt, and the only scientist whose authority could be expected to receive immediate notice from the head of the state was Einstein. Szilard and some others discussed the latest scientific data with him. All precise theory and calculation on the release of atomic energy starts from Einstein's discovery in 1905 of the equivalence of mass and energy. He was therefore qualified not only by general scientific eminence, but also as a technical expert in the particular subject, to offer an authoritative opinion on the implications of the latest experiments with uranium fission.

A few years before, he had been an absolute pacifist, and in spite of his discovery of the equivalence of mass and energy, had not believed that the large-scale release of atomic energy would be possible in his lifetime. He now felt himself compelled to admit that there were circumstances in which it is necessary to fight, and that it seemed probable that an atomic bomb could be made.

He sent his opinion in a famous letter, dated August 2nd, 1939, to President Roosevelt, one month before the Second World War started. In it he said : ' Some recent work by E. Fermi and L. Szilard . . . leads me to expect that the element uranium may be turned into a new and important source of energy in the immediate future. Certain aspects of the situation which has arisen seem to call for watchfulness and if necessary, quick action on the part of the administration . . .'

He referred in the letter to the possibility of an atomic bomb being carried into a port by a boat. If it exploded there, it ' might well destroy the whole port, together with some of the surrounding territory '. As a result of Einstein's letter, the President appointed the Director of the U.S. National Bureau of Standards, and representatives of the

U.S. Army and Navy to look after the interests of the U.S. Government in the matter.

The detailed solution of the release of atomic energy and its application in the atomic bomb was carried out by the younger generation of physicists, and of the hundreds who were involved, perhaps the most important contribution was made by Fermi.

When it became virtually certain in 1944 that the atomic bomb would work, the scientists engaged in its creation became deeply concerned with the moral and social problems involved in its use. Einstein and the others who had pressed at the beginning for intensified research on the possibility of the atomic bomb had had the aim of forestalling the Nazis, for they had been inclined to suppose that only the Nazis would dare to use such a barbaric weapon. They had the gravest misgivings when the American Government proceeded with the construction of the bomb without informing their Soviet allies, and they were horrified when it was used against the Japanese without warning.

The atomic scientists now formed a committee to explain the dangers of the situation to the world at large. Einstein accepted the chairmanship of this organization, and wrote in his appeal for support:

' Through the release of atomic energy, our generation has brought into the world the most revolutionary force since prehistoric man's discovery of fire.' He said that this basic power of the universe could not be fitted into the outmoded concepts of narrow nationalism, and there was no possibility of its control except through the aroused understanding and insistence of the peoples of the world. The atomic scientists recognized their inescapable responsibility to explain the facts of atomic energy and their social implications.

Einstein himself became a strong supporter of the idea

of One World. He held that in the light of the new knowledge, ' a world authority and an eventual world state are
not just *desirable* in the name of brotherhood, they are
necessary for *survival* '.

He saw ' no defence in science against this weapon which
can destroy civilization '. The only possible defence was not
in armaments, nor in science, nor in going underground,
but in law and order. He was of the opinion that there
were enough people of sound judgment and sense of justice
in the opposite camps capable and eager to work out a
practical system of control. The worst obstacle was the
prevention of such persons meeting in an informal manner,
for official negotiations could lead to success only after the
spadework of an informed nature had prepared the ground.
The conviction that a mutually satisfactory solution is possible must be gained first, and then the official negotiations
could be pursued with a fair promise of success.

He fought resolutely against the growth of cynicism.
When he was explaining in 1949 that he believed that the
very existence of humanity depended on the establishment
of a supernational organization, he was asked: ' Why are
you so earnestly opposed to the disappearance of the
human race? ' It would have been impossible, he thought,
for such a remark to have been made casually, a century
ago. The restoration of human morale had become of
supreme importance. ' To-day,' he said, ' everything that
has been acquired with such effort seems a razor in the
hands of a child of three.'

When President Truman proclaimed that the United
States would accelerate the work on the hydrogen bomb,
Einstein pointed out that if it were successful, ' radioactive
poisoning of the atmosphere, and hence annihilation of
any life on earth, has been brought within the range of
technical possibilities '. In the last analysis, the only effec-

tive way of dealing with the situation would depend primarily on mutual trust among men, and only secondarily on institutions.

The scientists had suffered a tragic fate. Striving in great sincerity for clarity and inner independence, through sheer superhuman efforts they had machined the tools which were being used to make them slaves and destroy them from within. They could not 'escape being muzzled by those who have political power in their hands'. Was there no escape for the scientists? Must they really tolerate and suffer all these indignities?

He concluded that if the scientists could find the time and courage to think honestly and critically over their situation and the tasks before them, and if they would act accordingly, then the possibilities for a sensible and satisfactory solution of the dangerous situation would be considerably improved.

When the U.S. Government began to make extreme difficulties over granting visas to travelling scientists, both American and foreign, he expressed the opinion that it had had 'significantly damaging effects' on the progress of science in the United States. He commented on the inhibiting effect of ubiquitous police activity on the freedom of scientific work, and said that it was necessary to overcome the obsession that the object of life in peacetime was to prepare for war. Until this had been accomplished, it would not be possible to concentrate on the real political problem which is: 'How can we contribute to make the life of man on this diminishing earth more secure and more tolerable?'

Even in 1954, at the age of seventy-five, he was still performing his scientist's moral duty, as he saw it. He advised American intellectuals not to testify before Senator McCarthy's committee, for he could 'see only the revolutionary way of non-co-operation. Every intellectual who is called before one of the committees ought to refuse to testify—that is, he must be prepared for gaol and economic ruin, the sacrifice of his personal welfare in the interests of the cultural welfare of his country '.

It was the moral duty of scientists to support with legal and material aid all of those among them who had suffered in this cause.

After many years of delicate health he died at Princeton on April 18th, 1955, occupying himself with the problems of science and peace, up to the day of his death. In collaboration with Bertrand Russell and six other eminent scientists, he prepared a declaration warning the world of the danger of hydrogen bomb warfare to the human race. He signed the declaration a few days before he died. Copies of this were sent to the heads of states, and there is little doubt that one of the reasons for the improved atmosphere which marked the Geneva Conference of July, 1955, was an appreciation of the implications of the hydrogen bomb, and that Einstein had a foremost part in impressing the reality of the danger on statesmen. His struggle for the responsible use of science continued to bear fruit even after his death, and will be an inspiration to future ages as well as our own.

While he was busying himself in his last hours with the noblest of all aims, the welfare of humanity, scientists were preparing the celebration of the fiftieth anniversary of his greatest discovery, the theory of relativity. While he was thinking about humanity, humanity was thinking about him. But he died just before the celebrations were due to take place. He bequeathed his brain for biological research, and his body was cremated.

So, at the end of his life, Einstein is seen as the heir of three thousand years of tradition. One part of his soul looked out with his brilliant eyes from the Old Testament and the Hebrew psalmists who celebrated the wonders of God's universe, and from the prophets who denounced man's wickedness and called on him to follow the moral injunctions of the Lord. The other part, the shy and gentle, placid and humorous, belonged to South Germany by birth and to Europe by education, interpreting with sublime brilliance the deepest subtleties which have been drawn out of nature by the experiments and calculations of modern science.

REFERENCES

The World as I see it, by Albert Einstein. John Lane: 1935.

Out of My Later Years, by Albert Einstein. Thames & Hudson: 1950.

Albert Einstein, by Anton Reiser. Thornton Butterworth: 1931.

Einstein, by Antonina Valentin. Weidenfeld & Nicolson: 1954.

Albert Einstein, by Leopold Infeld. Scribner: New York: 1950.

Albert Einstein, Edited by P. A. Schilpp. Tudor: New York: 1951.

Bulletin of the Atomic Scientists. Chicago.